WORKING MEN'S COLLEGE.
LIBRARY REGULATIONS.

BRITISH FLOODS AND DROUGHTS

By C. E. P. BROOKS, D.Sc.

The Evolution of Climate
    (*Second edition*)

Climate Through the Ages

The Weather

[*Photo: E. G. Bilham*

PLATE I—THE NORWICH FLOODS OF 1912

BRITISH FLOODS AND DROUGHTS

By C. E. P. BROOKS, D.Sc.

Honorary Secretary, Royal Meteorological Society,

AND

J. GLASSPOOLE, M.Sc., Ph.D.

Professional Associate, The Institution of Water Engineers.

With an Introductory Note

BY

HUGH ROBERT MILL, LL.D., D.Sc.

ERNEST BENN LIMITED

LONDON: BOUVERIE HOUSE, E.C.4

First Published in
1928
Printed
in
Great Britain

INTRODUCTORY NOTE

FOR seventy years the rainfall of the British Isles has been studied with steadily increasing diligence and effect, thanks to the insight and enthusiasm with which Mr. G. J. Symons planned and developed the British Rainfall Organization of voluntary observers.

When in the first year of the present century I was privileged to take part in the direction of the work, after the death of the founder, some 3,500 observers were sending in accurate and strictly comparable figures of daily or monthly rainfall. The methods initiated by my predecessor in their natural development raised this number to about 5,000 with no falling-off in the quality of the work, when the time came in 1919 for me to hand over control to the Meteorological Office. The statistical computations relied on by Mr. Symons had by then been strengthened by the cartographic and cartometric methods, which not only presented the distribution of rainfall in a graphic form but enabled quantitative measurements of great accuracy to be made, and furnished foundations and material for theoretical deductions.

Circumstances of health prevented me from carrying out the project of dealing comprehensively with the results which had been published annually in *British Rainfall*, but my former colleague, the late Mr. Carle Salter, discussed some aspects of the work in his able monograph, " The Rainfall of the British Isles," published in 1921.

It gives me great pleasure to find that Dr. Glasspoole, who was a member of the staff of the British Rainfall Organization before I left it, has joined forces with Dr. C. E. P. Brooks, long recognized as an authority on bygone meteorological conditions, in producing this work on British Floods and Droughts.

INTRODUCTORY NOTE

That the authors should desire a word of introduction from me is a source of no little gratification, for the breadth and originality of their treatment proves their mastery of the subject, and they might well have trusted their book to make its own way in the world. They have succeeded, by the discussion of recent occurrences which must be in the personal experience of most readers, in throwing light on the past. Early and even ancient descriptions of floods and droughts are interpreted by reference to relationships only recently discovered, so that we are enabled to know more of the meteorological conditions of England in previous centuries than the actual observers themselves. The authors have treated with lightness and grace a theme which most writers would have left heavy and uncouth. The happy literary presentment must result in stimulating interest in the fascinating study of the ways of the air.

The reader will of course distinguish between the vague and often exaggerated statements quoted from the early chroniclers, and the precise records of scientific observers. In particular he will note how the experiences of the past justify confidence in the probability of future extremes of lack or over-abundance of the treasures of the rain.

HUGH ROBERT MILL.

ACKNOWLEDGMENTS

A GOOD half of this book describes floods, great rains and droughts which have occurred during the twentieth and the closing decades of the nineteenth century, and in particular stress has been laid on the abnormal rains of the past ten years. While these years have been sufficiently prolific of weather vagaries, this emphasis is due rather to the great wealth of detail which we possess concerning them, and to the reason that, being fresh in our minds, they form a useful standard for comparison ; it does not mean that our fore-fathers were free from similar vagaries. The efficient recording of statistics of rainfall, by the British Rainfall Organization and the Meteorological Office, dates back little more than sixty years ; in fact it was a series of droughts in the years 1857, 1858 and 1859 which led the late Mr. G. J. Symons to commence in 1860 the regular collection of rain-fall data, out of which grew the British Rainfall Organization and the magnificent series of volumes under the title of *British Rainfall*. It is from these volumes, and from *Symons's Meteorological Magazine*, which was founded in 1866, that the great bulk of our information is ultimately derived ; a smaller amount comes from the maps and tables of the Monthly Weather Report issued by the Meteorological Office. In 1919 the British Rainfall Organization was incorporated in the Office, *British Rainfall* and the *Meteorological Magazine* becoming official publications.

The use of *British Rainfall* is facilitated by the indexes of the more important articles and tables, published in the volumes for 1900, pp. 23–45, and 1925, pp. 270–277.

Much of the abnormal weather of the past half-century has been the subject of papers at meetings of the Royal Meteorological Society. The drought of 1921 forms the subject of one such paper, in which we collaborated at the request of the Council, and we decided to abandon the purely descriptive methods which had previously been deemed sufficient, and to inquire into causes ; this paper forms the basis of Chapter VIII, while a similar inquest into the rains of 1924 reappears in Chapter I. We are indebted to the Council of the Society for permission to reproduce Fig. 8 from those papers, as well as Figs. 6 and 11 from a paper by J. Glasspoole, and Fig. 2 from one by J. Glasspoole and the late Mr. Carle Salter. Our thanks are also due to the Council of the Society for permission to reproduce the photograph which forms Plate II., and which was selected from the collection bequeathed to the Society by Mr. Symons, and to Mr. E. G. Bilham for that of the Norwich floods which forms the frontispiece. The influence of the Gulf Stream Drift and of Arctic Ice is discussed in greater detail in *Geophysical Memoirs*, Nos. 34 and 41, issued by the Meteorological Office.

The historical parts of the book derive from a great variety of sources, for both of us have collected such material for many years. The most important single source is Miss Ormerod's manuscript collection in the library of the Royal Meteorological Society, for the loan of which also we wish to thank the Council. Finally our thanks are due to Dr. H. R. Mill, for reading the manuscript and for giving us much useful advice, and to numerous other friends for assisting us with criticism and information.

CONTENTS

LIST OF ILLUSTRATIONS

THE RAINFALL OF THE BRITISH ISLES

" To talk of the weather is nothing but folly,
When it rains on the hill the sun shines in the valley."

OUR weather has been aptly described as made up of
" samples." We have a day or two of fine weather, a thunderstorm, a day or two of rain, and then perhaps a frost and
a fog. In the parlance of the forecaster the weather is " unsettled," an overworked word which means that for the time
being we are in the path of a series of barometric depressions.
Now and again a depression settles down for a week's stay,
and then the weather is settled wet, while at times an anticyclone or area of high pressure covers the British Isles and
no depressions pass this way at all, but for the most part a
depression appears to the westward, passes over or near
Britain, gives us a few hours of rain and passes away. The
next day is fine, and on the third another depression appears,
and so on. The British Isles are, in fact, on one of the storm
tracks of the globe.

Fortunately we are not on the main storm track but
rather to the south of it, on a branch line. The main track
lies a little to the south of Iceland, where the great depressions
pass majestically though somewhat slowly on their way.
They give us our prevailing south-west winds, and when
their path is nearer Scotland they often bring some quite
respectable totals of rain, especially in the north and west
of Scotland and Ireland, but they seldom bring really heavy
rains. They are generally accompanied on their southern
flank by one or more outriders in the shape of secondary
depressions, and these secondaries often bring an inch or
more of rain in a day, but the worst of our visitors from

the Atlantic are not the majestic Icelandic depressions
following one of the main tracks, but the fussy little fellows
which pass, sometimes rapidly along the English Channel,
sometimes across the heart of England. The Channel
depressions bring thunderstorms in summer, often snow
in winter ; the depressions which cross England bring some
of our heaviest falls of rain or snow. The great snowstorm
over Southern England on December 25th to 26th, 1927,
was due to a deep depression which passed up the Channel
on the evening of Christmas Day and the following night.
There are occasions when a depression does not travel
steadily eastward but follows an irregular course to and
fro across England. One of these errant visitors appeared
off Western Scotland on June 25th, 1927, followed a curved
path over the North Sea from the 26th to the 28th, and
moved southward across Scotland and Ireland in the last
days of June. On July 1st it moved eastward along the
English Channel, spent the whole of the 2nd over South-
East England, and did not finally move away in a north-
easterly direction until the 3rd. The week during which
this depression was following its many-looped track was
one of the rainiest of a very rainy summer.

It is obvious that where barometric depressions are most
frequent and most intense, barometric pressure must on
the average be lowest, and where barometric depressions are
least frequent, pressure must be highest. Hence on the
average pressure is lowest near Iceland and rises southward.
The highest average pressure is found away to the south-
west, beyond the Azores, where depressions are very rare
and the chief feature of the weather map is a persistent anticyclone. Fig. 1 shows the average or normal distribution
of pressure in the neighbourhood of the British Isles during
the year. The important features for our weather are the
" Icelandic low " in the north-west and the " Azores anticyclone " in the south-west, and these two are termed " centres
of action " ; between them lies a neutral region of west
and south-west winds.

These prevailing west and south-west winds introduce

us to another cause of rain besides the passage of barometric depressions. There is no need here to go in great detail into the physical processes which result in rain ; it is sufficient to remark that the only way in which an appreciable quantity of rain can be produced in nature is by the raising of moist air to a higher level. A barometric depression or cyclone is a great natural engine for raising air from near the earth's surface to the higher regions of the atmosphere.

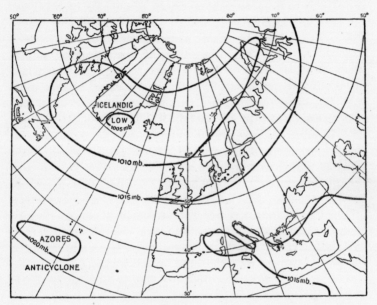

FIG 1.—AVERAGE PRESSURE DISTRIBUTION, YEAR

Warm air from lower latitudes travels up great sloping banks of colder air from higher latitudes, or else a wedge of cold air pushes under the warm air and raises it bodily. An interesting example is described in the *Meteorological Magazine* for February, 1928 ; in this case air which rested on the surface of the Atlantic Ocean near the Azores on June 30th, 1924, was traced to an altitude of 12,000 feet above Belgium thirty-six hours later. That is why barometric depressions bring rain, but there are other ways in

which moist air can be forced to rise. One of them is the
sufficiently obvious way of placing in the path of an air-
current an obstacle, such as a range of hills. The rainiest
regions of the world, the Khasi Hills of Assam, the Western
Ghats of India, the volcanic mountains of the Hawaii Islands,
and the Cameroons of West Africa, are all found where a
warm moist wind steadily blows against a range of mountains. In a slightly lesser degree the same situation is realized
in these islands, where the Western Highlands of Scotland,
the fells of Cumberland, and the mountains of Snowdonia
stand out in the path of the moist winds from the Atlantic.
The rain which is caused by the winds rising over mountains
in this way is called *orographic* rain, as the rain which falls
in barometric depressions or cyclones is called *cyclonic* rain.

In the following chapters we shall at times be concerned
with yet a third type of rainfall, which is associated mainly
with summer showers and thunderstorms. These are similar
to cyclones in that the rain is caused by warm air being
replaced at the surface by colder air, but the beginning of
the process is different. Whereas cyclones arise from the
coming together of two great currents of air at different
temperatures, thundery showers arise most readily in calm
or only slightly drifting air. Summer thunderstorms are of
two main types. The first results from the warming up of
the lower layers of air by ground heated by the summer sun ;
when the air becomes sufficiently hot it rises through the
overlying layers of less heated air. This process brings about
the " thundery showers " and sporadic thunderstorms which
develop out of a clear sky and seem to have such a special
penchant for school treats and picnic parties. When conditions are suitable the warmed air from a large area may
flow into a comparatively small space and rise there, producing rainfalls of several inches in a short time, which are
sometimes known as " cloudbursts." They are, however,
very local, and they produce but an insignificant proportion
of the rainfall over the country as a whole.

The second type of thunderstorm is intermediate between
these casual outbursts and the widespread rains which

accompany large cyclonic depressions. It frequently happens in summer and autumn that when a depression is advancing from the Atlantic directly towards these islands, after one or more days of fine weather, a warm moist south-east wind sets in near the ground, while the upper layers of air are still cold, either because the upper wind is still blowing from the north, or because the air at high levels originally came from the north and has not yet had time to warm up. This condition of affairs is especially favourable for the occurrence of thunderstorms, for the lower layer of air is light enough to rise violently when it has the chance to do so, but moving in such large horizontal sheets, the opportunity only comes where some local circumstance, such as a favourable upward slope or a patch of warm ground, gives it a start. Hence a whole series of thunderstorms may begin at nearly the same time in different places, and drift slowly across the country along parallel lines. The type of pressure distribution which brings about this condition is well known to weather forecasters, and when it is highly developed a forecast of " thunder " is reasonably safe, though the credit which accrues depends largely on whether or no a storm happens to strike London or one of the larger holiday resorts. When widespread thunderstorms of this second type occur several times in a month, they contribute a large quantity of rainfall, and may cause the whole month to be classed as wet even though the amount of cyclonic rainfall in the narrower sense was small.

These three types, *cyclonic*, *orographic* and *thunderstorm*, or as it is technically called, *instability* precipitation, together make up practically the whole amount of the water which falls on the British Isles in the form of rain, snow and hail, and it is readily seen that the distribution of the annual totals depends to a very large extent on the distribution of the causes which give rise to them. The tracks of barometric depressions are almost independent of the configuration of the ground, at least up to the modest elevations which are reached by the " mountains " of Britain. When we are dealing with the Alps or the Rockies, it is a different

B

matter, but so far as is known, not even the Western Highlands or Snowdonia can turn a depression from its path. Hence we should expect cyclonic rainfall to be independent of configuration, and, strictly speaking, that is what happens. The rainfall during the passage of a depression is usually somewhat heavier on high ground than on the lowlands, but that is because the storm winds have to climb the high ground like any other winds, and in hilly country there is some orographic rain mixed up with the cyclonic rain. Even so, however, the rainfall associated with a large depression does not usually differ very much in different parts of its track, and it is quite possible that some of the lowlands will receive more than the neighbouring hills.

It is very different with orographic rain. It happens that the areas of highest ground in the British Isles are almost all near the western coasts, on the side from which the prevailing winds blow, and especially the prevailing moisture-bearing winds. Since the orographic rainfall is generally heavier on the windward side than on the leeward side, this means that nearly all the areas of heavy average rainfall are close to the western coasts of Britain and Ireland, and especially the former, where the mountains are so much the higher. Some measure of the importance of the orographic effect may be understood when we consider that the rainfall on the west coast, which at sea-level amounts to 35 or 40 inches, has doubled itself at a height of 1,000 to 1,500 feet, and at still greater heights may be three or four times the fall at sea-level. Some of these mountain regions receive a regular rainfall of 160 or more inches a year, an amount which even the most severe succession of cyclonic storms and thunderstorms is unable to equal over the lowlands to the east.

As a rule in Britain the rainfall increases with height on the windward slopes right up to the summit. When the ground slopes very steeply upwards, the air may have sufficient upward impetus to go on rising for some distance after it has passed the summit, and the region of heaviest rain may then occur a short distance down the leeward

slope. An example of this is the Stye, at the head of Borrowdale, in Cumberland, which with an average annual rainfall
of 170 inches is one of the wettest places in Europe, although
the rain-gauge is at the modest height of 1,070 feet. This
heavy rainfall is really due to the uprush of air over the
summit of Great Gable, which lies a short distance to the
westward. The effect is partly caused by the raindrops
being actually blown over the summit by the winds, and
falling in the relatively calm area in the shelter of the mountain. Even Seathwaite, farther down the valley, at a height
of only 422 feet, has an average rainfall of 129 inches.

Thunderstorm or instability rains fall by preference over
areas of level ground or low hills, some distance from the
sea. They are best developed in the Midlands and the
southern half of England, where they add appreciably to
the annual totals of rain, but although some of the individual
falls associated with thunderstorms are unsurpassed in this
country, the total effect cannot compete with the more
regular orographic rainfall of the west.

A map of the average annual rainfall over the British Isles
shows the combination of these three sources of rainfall,
cyclonic, orographic and instability. Such a map is shown in
Fig. 2, which represents the average for the thirty-five year
period 1881 to 1915. There is a special reason for choosing
a period of thirty-five years, about which more will be said
later (Chapter XIV), and the particular interval shown on the
map has been adopted as the official standard in this country.
A map for any other period of ten or more consecutive years
would, however, show the same general features, though the
details would be slightly different. A glance at the map
suffices to show the great extent to which it is dominated by
the orographic rainfall. There are three outstanding areas,
each of which has a fall of more than 100 inches a year, and
these coincide with the three areas of greatest elevation, the
Western Highlands of Scotland, the mountains of Cumberland, and the region of Snowdonia. The whole range of the
Pennines forms a region of relatively heavy rainfall (more
than 40 inches a year), which contrasts strongly with the

dry areas of the Dee Valley to the west, and central Yorkshire to the east, while the Lincolnshire wolds form another
region of relatively heavy rain. In fact a close scrutiny of

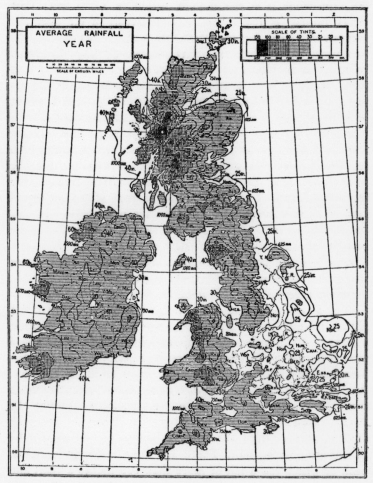

FIG. 2—DISTRIBUTION OF AVERAGE ANNUAL RAINFALL FOR
THIRTY-FIVE YEARS

the map side by side with a relief map will show a relationship between elevation and rainfall which holds almost
without exception.

The second obvious feature of the map is the general
decrease of rainfall from west to east. This is also in a sense
due to orographic control ; the mountains being mainly
near the west coasts and the prevailing winds being south-
westerly, the air becomes considerably drier by the time it
has reached the east coast than it is when it first strikes the
land in the west. It is true that occasionally a good deal of
rain falls along the east coast with an east wind, but it is
most probable that even in these cases the water vapour
originally came from the Atlantic, and that the fall would
have been a good deal heavier had the air not parted with
much of its moisture in crossing the British Isles. Moreover, this east wind rainfall is also typically orographical in
its distribution, being heavier on the hills than along the
coast itself. East winds persisted during the greater part
of December, 1927, and there was a reversal of the usual
type of distribution, more than 3 inches falling in parts of
the east of Aberdeenshire and Forfarshire, and only half an
inch in considerable areas of the mountains of Inverness-
shire. This type of distribution rarely persists for periods of
more than a few days, however, and does little to modify
the general decrease of rainfall from west to east.

This general decrease is shown not only by Ireland and
Great Britain separately, but also by the British Isles as a
whole. In Ireland there are only two small areas which have
a rainfall of less than 30 inches a year, a tiny patch in the
Shannon Valley, and a somewhat larger area near Dublin
on the east coast. The greater part of the country has a
rainfall of 40 to 60 inches, and there are several large tracts
in the west where the latter figure is exceeded. In Scotland
the rainfall is as high or higher in the west, but there is a
narrow strip along almost the whole of the east coast with
a rainfall of less than 30 inches. This relatively dry strip
broadens southward to include the whole eastern half of
England, being widest across the Midlands. Small parts of
the latter, and quite considerable areas near the east coast,
have less than 25 inches, and a strip of the Essex coast,
which is the driest part of the British Isles, receives just

under 20 inches a year. Near the south coast, owing to the
influence of rain-bearing southerly winds, the amounts
increase again.

The orographic control dominates our rainfall to such an
extent that a very close study of the average map is required
to discover any effects which can be attributed to variations
of cyclonic or thunderstorm rains from place to place. With
regard to cyclonic rainfall this is only to be expected, for by
its nature it is spread almost evenly over the country, and
forms a basis to which other types of rainfall are added to
produce the irregularities in the distribution of rainfall
actually observed. It seems certain, however, that this basis
of cyclonic rain is not everywhere exactly the same, even
when an average over many years is considered, but increases
from east to west or from south-east to north-west. This
general increase can be illustrated by giving the average
annual rainfall at a number of places along the coast in a
south-east to north-west direction over the British Isles :

County	Station	Average Rainfall
		inches
Essex - - - -	Shoeburyness - - -	20
Kent - - - -	Dungeness - - -	24
Dorset - - -	Portland Bill - - -	27
Pembroke - - -	St. David's - - -	37
Anglesey - - -	Holyhead - - -	35
Cumberland - -	Whitehaven - - -	42
Argyll - - -	Mull of Kintyre - -	41
Argyll - - -	Tiree - - - -	48
Inverness - - -	Monach - - - -	47
Mayo - - - -	Blacksod Point - -	50

A north-westward increase in the amount of cyclonic rain
would be the natural result of the decrease in barometric
pressure and increase in the frequency and intensity of
depressions in that direction, but it is largely masked by the
much greater increase in the amount of orographic rainfall.

The effect of thunderstorm rains in a map of average
rainfall is even more difficult to distinguish than the effect of

cyclonic rains. Thunderstorms are not confined to any particular areas, though they are somewhat more frequent
inland than on the coast, and it may be considered that
superposed on the orographic and cyclonic rainfall we have
a layer of thunderstorm rains distributed more or less uniformly over the whole land surface, but somewhat heavier
in inland districts than near the coast.

The varying controls of rainfall in Britain are somewhat
more clearly seen in the averages of the different months
and seasons than in the map of annual rainfall, for the
different effects, orographic, cyclonic, and instability, reach
their greatest intensity at different times of the year. The
amount of orographic rain depends on the strength and
regularity of the west and south-west winds, which in turn
are governed by the difference of pressure between the
Azores anticyclone and the Icelandic low. The Azores anticyclone varies comparatively little through the year, but the
Icelandic low is much more intense in winter than in
summer ; in fact it almost disappears during the latter
season. Hence the orographic rainfall varies regularly through
the year from a maximum near mid-winter to a minimum
near mid-summer. This type of variation is clearly shown
by the rainfall at Glenquoich, Inverness-shire, illustrated in
the upper diagram of Fig. 3. It should be noted that the
vertical scale employed for Glenquoich is only half that for
the other two stations.

It is much more difficult to find a clear example of the
dominating control of rainfall by the cyclonic component.
Obviously we have to look for such an example in comparatively flat country, in a region of few thunderstorms.
East Anglia is flat, but has a fair number of thunderstorms ;
Northern Scotland has few thunderstorms, but cannot be
described as flat. The example finally chosen was Worstead,
in Norfolk, shown in the middle diagram of Fig. 3. The
month of greatest rainfall is October, when cyclonic rainfall
is generally greatest over the whole country. The second
wettest month is July, which owes its prominence to instability rains, but November (cyclonic) has almost as much.

The fourth and fifth places are shared by August (instability) and December (cyclonic). It will be noticed that the year's rainfall at Worstead is less than that at either of the other two stations illustrated in Fig. 3.

It is almost as difficult to find a good example of the control of rainfall by thunderstorms. Here again we must select a fairly flat district, but one near the centre of the

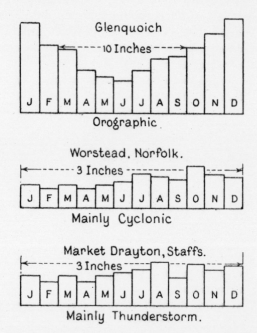

FIG. 3—TYPES OF ANNUAL VARIATION OF RAINFALL

country where thunderstorms are frequent. The example selected was Market Drayton, in Staffordshire, shown in the lowest diagram of Fig. 3. The wettest month is August, when instability rains are heaviest, but the cyclonic component is not lacking, and gives second place to October. July, the other month of thunderstorms, comes only fourth.

We have dwelt at considerable length on these different controls of rainfall because in the following chapters it will be seen that a season of abnormally heavy rain may be due to the marked development of any one of them. We have in fact learnt to classify months or seasons according to the particular element which predominates. Thunderstorms rarely give their distinctive character to the whole season ; they tend to grade into the cyclonic type, but the distinction between seasons of cyclonic and orographic rains is very far from being academic. It is a real distinction, both in its natural causes and in its economic effects, and it happens surprisingly rarely that we are at a loss which term to apply and have to classify the rainfall as " indefinite " in type.

PART I

GREAT RAINS AND FLOODS

CHAPTER I

THE CAUSES OF PERSISTENT RAIN

" Fifty times have I wished this very day, that Dr. Darwin's scheme of giving rudders and sails to the Ice Islands, that spoil all our summers, were actually put into practice."—COWPER (1792).

IN the Introduction a brief account was given of the circumstances in which rain falls in the British Isles, and it was explained that the greater part of the year's total falls either during the passage of barometric depressions or as a result of moist winds from the Atlantic blowing against the coasts and uplands. Going back a little further, it is seen that both barometric depressions and westerly winds are related to the position and intensity of the Azores anticyclone and the Icelandic low (see Fig. 1). Nearly all our abnormal seasons can be traced to some irregularity of one or other of these centres of action ; as a rule, both are concerned. The two centres in fact are not independent of each other, but have some curious and important relationships. In the first place, they are to some extent *complementary* ; when the Azores anticyclone is more intense than usual the Icelandic low is deeper than usual, and then our westerly winds are unusually strong. When one is weak the other is generally weak also, and our westerly winds are light and irregular. Sometimes for several days or a week or two they disappear, the

Icelandic low being replaced by an anticyclone and the Azores high by an area of low pressure ; when that happens we get persistent easterly winds instead of westerly. In February, 1895, pressure was higher over Iceland than over the Azores during the whole month, and we had a long spell of strong east and north-east winds, which brought some of the coldest weather on record in these islands. Secondly, although they are thus in a sense opposites, the Azores anticyclone and the Icelandic low are both part of the North Atlantic system of pressure, or, to use Sir Gilbert Walker's term, the " North Atlantic Oscillation," and they tend to keep the same distance apart. Thus, when one moves north, so very often does the other, and the weather associated with them moves with them. If the whole system moves northward, the British Isles come more under anticyclonic conditions, depressions are very rare, and a period of fine dry weather results. If, on the other hand, the whole system moves southward, the main track of the barometric depressions passes close to or even directly across these islands, and we are in for a period of wet, stormy weather.

It would be going rather outside the scope of this book, besides being a very large undertaking, to discuss adequately the causes for these variations of intensity and changes of position of the centres of action. In fact the material for a complete discussion is not yet available, and the most that we can do is to refer to some of the more important influences which seem to affect our weather, and to indicate the various ways in which we believe that they produce their effects. In the first place, it may be said that both Azores anticyclone and Icelandic low are part of the world circulation of the air, which results from the difference of temperature between the Equatorial regions and the Polar regions, combined with the rotation of the earth on its axis. The air which is withdrawn from the neighbourhood of Iceland to cause the Icelandic low is, so to speak, dumped in the neighbourhood of the Azores to form an anticyclone. Similar pairs of related centres are found in other parts of the world ; for example, the anticyclone in about 30° latitude in the

North Pacific and the low pressure area which develops every winter near the Aleutian Islands of Alaska. In these pairs of related centres, it nearly always happens that when pressure in one becomes higher than usual, that in the other becomes lower than usual, and *vice versa*.

While the existence of the Azores anticyclone and Icelandic low undoubtedly depends on the general circulation of the earth's atmosphere, it is much less certain that the greatest variations in their intensity are the result of variations of this general circulation. If this were so, we should expect a close similarity between variations of pressure in the Aleutian and Icelandic lows, or in the North Pacific and North Atlantic anticyclones. Some similarity there is, but it is slight, and can only be demonstrated by refined mathematical tests. There is no such obvious relationship as the opposition between the Azores anticyclone and Icelandic low, which can easily be seen by a mere inspection of the average pressures of a succession of months, without any mathematical aids at all.

When we come to consider the causes of droughts, however, we shall find that there may be circumstances in which an exceptionally powerful atmospheric circulation is able to dominate the pressure distribution over the whole northern hemisphere. When this happens, pressure in the Arctic regions becomes abnormally low and the whole system of high and low pressure areas in the northern hemisphere advances northward. This gives us dry weather, but the reverse condition of an abnormally weak atmospheric circulation does not necessarily cause the Icelandic low and Azores anticyclone to advance southward. Probably it merely has the effect of making the pressure distribution unstable, and so allowing more local causes to come into play.

Hence it seems that we must look nearer home for the causes of the distribution of pressure which give rise to our abnormally rainy seasons. Among such local causes (using the word " local " in contrast to " world-wide," and not in any parochial sense) two are known to have an appreciable effect on our weather namely, the Gulf Stream, with its continuation the Gulf Stream Drift, or North Atlantic Drift, which carries the warm water from the Gulf of Mexico towards the coasts of Western Europe, and the ice in the Arctic Ocean and the Greenland Seas. It has been found that when the Gulf Stream is weaker and less warm than usual, pressure tends to become lower than usual in the Azores anticyclone and to the north and north-eastwards over Ireland, England and France. There is, however, very little indication of any systematic change in the pressure near Iceland, which may become lower, but may instead become slightly higher, and it seems evident that the tendency of the barometer to become lower farther south, which is most marked over the British Isles and Northern France, is really due to a southward shift of the whole North Atlantic pressure system. The main paths of barometric depressions are also shifted southward, and consequently a decrease in the strength of the Gulf Stream tends to bring a period of wet, stormy weather over the greater part of the British Isles. It is necessary to say that it tends to do so, instead of saying that it actually does, because the Gulf Stream is only one of the numerous factors at work in the complexity of British weather, and the unfavourable conditions resulting from a weak Gulf Stream may easily be overweighted by favourable conditions resulting from other factors.

Whether the wet season resulting from a weak Gulf Stream will be cyclonic or orographic in type depends on the amount of the southward shift of the Icelandic low. If this shift is sufficiently marked to bring the main storm tracks right across Southern Ireland and England, or even farther south over the Channel, a season of cyclonic type will result. On these occasions pressure in Iceland not infrequently becomes abnormally high, and with a weakening of the south-westerly winds the amount of orographic rainfall in the Western Highlands of Scotland is less than usual. The greater part of the wet summer of 1924 was of the cyclonic type, and probably the main cause was a weakening of the Gulf Stream as a result of a falling off of the south-east trade wind during 1923. On other occasions, however, it seems that the southward shift is of smaller extent, and the barometric depressions, though somewhat south of their regular tracks, still pass for the most part to the north-west and north of the British Isles. On these occasions pressure over Iceland is commonly lower than usual, the south-west winds are exceptionally strong and stormy, and the rainy season is of the orographic type. The wet winter and spring of 1919 to 1920 were of this type. Which of the two types, cyclonic or orographic, will prevail seems to depend on other factors, such as the amount and distribution of Arctic ice, and probably also on the general distribution of pressure in other parts of the world.

The temperature of the Gulf Stream off Newfoundland is considerably lowered by the cold Labrador Current which flows from Davis Strait along the coast of Labrador to the Newfoundland Banks, carrying great quantities of ice. The amount of ice varies greatly from year to year; in 1912, the year in which the *Titanic* was lost after striking an ice-berg, the amount of ice was exceptionally great, but in other years, such as 1924, there was comparatively little ice. Thanks to the researches of Lieut.-Commander E. H. Smith, of the International Ice Patrol, the causes of these variations are now fairly well understood, and it is found that the chief cause of a strong and heavily ice-laden Labrador Current is a persistent north-west wind along the coast of Labrador. We should naturally expect a strong, cold Labrador Current to have a similar effect on the pressure distribution over the eastern North Atlantic to that which results from a weak, cool Gulf Stream ; that is to say, we should expect a period of strong north-west winds on the Labrador coast to be followed by wet weather in the British Isles. In fact we find that out of the thirteen wettest seasons between 1879 and 1924, no fewer than nine were immediately preceded by a period of such strong north-west winds. The most notable examples of wet seasons which can be attributed mainly to this cause were January to March, 1903, April to June, 1907, and March to May, 1913, all of which were of the orographical type, and June to August, 1912, which was of the cyclonic type. Thus, as with a weak Gulf Stream, the

C

actual type of pressure distribution and rainy season which follows a strong Labrador current appears to depend on other factors.

Part of the effect of the cold Labrador Current is due to ice from the American Arctic Archipelago, but the main part of the Arctic ice lies farther east. Under the term " Arctic " we include first of all the great mass of thick ice which occupies the larger part of the North Polar Basin, and extends every winter to the northern coasts of Asia and of European Russia. This ice drifts gradually in the direction of Greenland, and every spring large masses of it pass into the East Greenland Current and travel southward along the coast of Greenland. Some of this ice reaches Iceland ; more of it rounds Cape Farewell and enters Baffin Bay, where it is gradually dispersed.

While the influence of the Gulf Stream on the distribution of pressure appears to be greatest to the southward of the British Isles, that of Arctic ice, as would be expected, is concentrated more in northerly regions. It is also far more complicated than the Gulf Stream effect, since it varies greatly from one season to another.

Ice has a great power of cooling the air above it, and since cold air is heavier than warm air, it follows that barometric pressure tends to be increased by the presence of a large amount of floating ice. Examination of a long series of observations from Iceland has shown that in spring months in which there is a large amount of ice in the seas near that island, the average pressure is considerably higher than in years when there is no ice. This increase of pressure over Iceland is brought about not so much by a decrease in the intensity of the Icelandic low as by a southward shift towards the British Isles. When it is well developed, this state of affairs leads to a highly characteristic distribution of pressure. A large anticyclone covers the neighbourhood of Iceland, while to the south of it, across or near the British Isles, there is a belt of low pressure along which barometric depressions pass at frequent intervals. It will be readily appreciated that this state of affairs is extremely unfortunate for British weather ; it is usually very persistent, and so long as it continues there is no hope of any fine spell lasting for more than a day or so. It is this pressure distribution which gives us our best (or worst) examples of the cyclonic type of rainfall distribution, and when it occurs in spring or summer, it is highly probable that Arctic ice, generally near Iceland or in the Greenland Sea, has something to do with it. A notable example was the wet summer of 1918, which greatly impeded the progress of affairs in Flanders. In the spring months of that year there was an abnormal quantity of ice in the East Greenland Current, while Iceland was heavily beset. Greenland Sea ice also appears to have been a contributory cause to the wet summer of 1912, though in that year Iceland itself was comparatively free.

After about June the ice masses which have been floating in the sea off Iceland and Southern Greenland disappear, but the evil which they do lives after them. A good deal of the cold water which results from the melting of the ice drifts into the north-eastern North Atlantic, where it becomes mixed with the warmer water of the Gulf Stream Drift. It may be that streaks and patches of colder water lie among the warm, giving rapid variations of temperature in short distances, a condition which is very favourable to the formation of barometric depressions in the Atlantic, or it may be that the mere cooling of the surface waters is sufficient, but whatever the reason, there is a strong tendency for spring and early summer months in which there has been a great deal of Arctic ice to be followed by a very stormy period in the British Isles during the autumn and winter. The most notable example of this was the wet autumn of 1882 and winter of 1882–3, which followed one of the worst ice-years on record in the Greenland Sea. The year 1911 was a very bad ice-year at Iceland, the shore being blocked for long periods (a situation which had something to do with the abnormal weather of that year), and this was followed by a wet winter from November, 1911, to March, 1912. Both 1882–83 and 1911–12 were of the cyclonic type, and this seems to be the general rule for these wet seasons of autumn and winter which follow on ice-rich springs and summers in the Arctic.

This does not by any means exhaust the various factors which go to make up the vagaries of British weather. But whereas we are beginning to have some understanding of the way in which the Gulf Stream, the Labrador Current and the Arctic ice " work," with regard to other factors we have only the merest glimmerings. Some of the connexions which have been discovered seem at first sight almost bizarre. For example, a poor Nile flood in summer is often followed in the succeeding winter and early spring by low pressure over Iceland, the Faroes and South-Western Norway, a distribution which favours heavy orographical rain. The exceedingly heavy rain of the first three months of 1903 was a notable example. A good Nile flood, on the other hand, tends to be followed by high pressure to the north of the British Isles, giving a winter of very cold east winds. The first two months of 1895 followed one of the highest Nile floods on record. It is not possible that the amount of water in the Nile should directly influence the subsequent weather over the British Isles, yet the connexion discovered by Mr. E. W. Bliss, formerly of the Egyptian Meteorological Service, appears to be beyond question. The only solution is that the Nile floods (and the rainfall in Abyssinia of which they are the direct result) and British weather both depend on some third factor. What that original cause is we do not know, though it seems probable that it is in some way connected with the general circulation of the atmosphere.

Another element which seems to have some relationship with our weather is the depth of the winter snowfall over Northern Europe, and the way in which the snow-cover lasts into spring. This relationship was discovered by the late Swedish meteorologist, H. H. Hildebrandsson, and a further examination shows that there is a tendency for a deep, persistent snow-cover to be followed by abnormally high pressure over the continent of Europe during the following summer and autumn. In spring and summer of the same year there is a tendency for low pressure over the Azores, and in autumn for unusually low pressure near Iceland. The effect of a deep snow-cover is thus rather similar to that of much Arctic ice, and as the two phenomena tend to occur together, it would seem probable that the snow-cover may occasionally aid the ice in giving us a wet summer or autumn. It is not likely that the snow-cover by itself can do much damage to British weather.

Another curious relationship, knowledge of which we owe to the Austrian meteorologist, A. Defant (meteorology is a truly international science !), is with volcanic eruptions. Defant found that a series of great volcanic eruptions which occur at short intervals of time, or even a single eruption of outstanding magnitude, like that of Krakatoa in 1883, disturbs the usual distribution of pressure over the North Atlantic for a period of several years. The first result is a rise of pressure in the Icelandic low and a fall of pressure in the Azores anticyclone, giving a tendency for a decrease in the amount of orographic rainfall and an increase in the amount of cyclonic rainfall. This condition lasts for about a year after the eruption and is then followed by a swing of the pendulum to the opposite extreme, a deepening of the Icelandic low and an intensification of the Azores anticyclone. The cause is believed to be not the violence of the explosion, but the large amount of dust thrown up into the air, which interferes with the free passage of the sun's rays. The main volcanic eruptions during the period discussed by Defant were : Krakatoa in 1883, Taravera and Ninafu in 1886, Ritter Island and Bandai San in 1888, and St. Maria, St. Vincent and Mont Pele in 1902. There was also the eruption of Katmai in Alaska in 1912. The results as far as they affect this country have not yet been worked out in detail, but we may note that of the years in which the eruptions occurred, 1883, 1886 and 1912 were all distinctly wet, 1888 was normal, but 1902 was dry. Of the years following the eruptions, 1884, 1887, 1889 and 1913 were dry, 1887 being the driest year of the nineteenth century, but 1903 was outstandingly wet. If we look at

the distribution of the rainfall in the different years we find
that, in the years of eruptions, 1886 and 1912 were cyclonic,
but the remaining years 1883, 1888 and 1902 were indefinite.
Of the years following eruptions, 1884, 1887 and 1912 had
an orographical type of distribution, 1889 was indefinite
and 1903 was cyclonic. The agreement with Defant's views
about the changes of pressure which follow volcanic eruptions
is fairly good, but is spoilt by the years 1902 and 1903, which
are in direct opposition to the variations in the remaining
years. It is curious that if, instead of 1902 and 1903, we
take the two years 1903 and 1904, the latter year being dry
with an orographical type of distribution, the agreement
becomes almost complete, suggesting that the exceptionally
violent volcanic outbreaks of 1902 did not take effect until
the following years.

When we go back into the earlier years, however, the
variations of rainfall following volcanic eruptions were not
nearly so regular. Between 1755 and 1875 there were twelve
years with important volcanic eruptions, namely, 1755, 1766,
1783, 1785, 1789, 1808, 1812, 1815, 1831, 1835, 1872 and
1875. Of these twelve years, five were wetter than the average
and seven were drier; while of the twelve succeeding years,
four were wetter and eight were drier. Even the great eruptions of Asama in 1783 and Tomboro in 1815 were not
followed by anything remarkable in the way of drought or
heavy rainfall, though the latter eruption is credited with
the abnormal cold of 1816, " the year without a summer."
It seems, therefore, that we must be sceptical as to the part
played by volcanic eruptions in the variations of our weather.

From all this it will be seen that the influences at work
on British weather are many and exceedingly diverse. That
is unfortunate in that it greatly increases the difficulty of
forecasting the weather for any period longer than 24 hours,
but in another way it may be fortunate. Among so many
factors some will tend towards fine weather and others
towards rainy weather, and these more or less balance each
other. The greater the number of factors, the smaller is
the probability that there will be a large preponderance

on one side or the other for a long period. This multitude of factors may therefore play an important part in maintaining the famous equability and moderation of our weather. We may complain of a drought, but how often does a drought bring personal discomfort to anyone in Britain, in spite of our enormous daily waste of water? Our memories of 1921, the driest year in England since 1788, perhaps since 1741, are now almost entirely memories of a pleasant season of fine weather. We may complain of heavy rains and flood, but how many people do our rivers drive out of house and home in even the rainiest year? With regard to the ups and downs of our rainfall, we can say as the Red Queen might have said : " I could show you floods, in comparison with which you'd call that a drought." (" No, I shouldn't," said Alice . . . " a flood can't be a drought, you know. That would be nonsense. . . .")

CHAPTER II

THE WET YEAR 1927—THE TURN OF THE TIDE?

" The spring, the summer,
The childing autumn, angry winter, change
Their wonted liveries, and the mazed world
By their increase, now knows not which is which."
(SHAKESPEARE, *A Midsummer Night's Dream*

AFTER five successive years of unusually heavy rainfall, had we a right to expect an improvement in 1927? It seems reasonable to say that since every wet spell must end some time, the longer it has lasted the more chance there is of the next year being fine. Rainfall is often unreasonable, however, and an examination of the figures for the past two hundred years leads to a rather curious result. If after a dry year, either standing alone or the last of a series, there comes a year wetter than the average, the odds are more than two to one in favour of the third year being dry, but if this third year should turn out to be wet, then the betting is slightly in favour of the fourth year being wet also. If a wet spell has already lasted for two or more years, it is rather more probable that the coming year will be wet than that it will be dry. Hence all that statistics could say was that 1927 was rather more likely to be wet than dry. The hopes of a dry year were brighter at the beginning of 1923 than they have been ever since. The rules about dry years are different. If one or more wet years have been followed by a dry year, the odds are three to two in favour of the following year being dry also, but after two successive dry years the odds are that the third year will be wet. After three or more dry years, the chances of the next year being wet or dry are about even.

During the present century wet weather has prevailed.

Since 1906 only six out of twenty-one years have received a rainfall below the average, and 1921 was the only year with a marked deficiency. Including 1927, the mean annual rainfall of the twenty-two years was 4 per cent. in excess of the average, giving an accumulated excess over the country generally very nearly equal to the rainfall of a whole year, so that in twenty-two years we have had nearly twenty-three years' rainfall. There is another way of looking at the problem, which is more hopeful. Since the present spell of six wet years has only once been exceeded, it is reasonable to expect a return to more normal conditions within the next few years. Again, since previous long runs of wet years have almost invariably been followed by a series in which dry years have predominated, it is not unduly optimistic to hope that the present run will soon break down and that the accumulated excess of rainfall will be wiped off in due course.

However, it is useless to prophesy after the event, and the event was sufficiently dismal, for over the British Isles as a whole 1927 was wetter than any year since 1903, although in Scotland and Ireland 1927 was not quite so wet as 1924. The average falls and their percentages of the average for the years 1881 to 1915 are given in the *Meteorological Magazine* for January, 1928, as follows :

	Amount	Per cent. of Average
	inches	
England and Wales - -	43·3	123
Scotland - - - -	57·4	114
Ireland - - - -	46·7	108
British Isles - - -	48·8	118

The abundant rainfall was not confined to any particular season, though it slacked off to some extent towards the end of the year, for the only months which did not exceed the average were May, October and December. The worst months came in summer and early autumn—June, August

and September. During the latter month England and
Wales received no less than two and one-third times their
normal September fall, and those who had deferred their
holidays because of the bad weather found that they had
jumped out of the puddle into the pond.

One of the peculiar features of the recent run of wet
years is that while at first wet winters predominated, in the
last few years it has been the summers which were abnormally
wet. With only one exception, each of the nine successive
winter half-years, beginning with that of 1911 to 1912, was
wetter than usual. Subsequently each of the six summers
since that of 1922 was very wet, especially those of 1924
and 1927. This alternation of a run of wet winters with a
run of wet summers is characteristic of our rainfall ; it will
be further discussed in Chapter XIV.

The abnormality of recent years is also shown by statistics
of " rain-days." The rain-day is a day on which ·01 inch
or more of rain is recorded. Some indication of what this
amounts to is afforded by comparing it to ten minutes'
continuous rain at London or five minutes' at Seathwaite,
in the English Lake District, the rain falling in each case
at the average rate for the locality. While therefore a rain-
day includes some days with too little rain to be of importance for many practical purposes, each rain-day receives
a precipitation which, if concentrated into a few minutes of
the day, would be quite noticeable. During the thirty-five
years 1881 to 1915 the average number of rain-days at stations
representative of the British Isles was 204. In 1927 the
number was 223, or nineteen rain-days more than the average,
and in each year since the dry year 1921 the number of days
with rain has been in excess of the average. During the last
twelve years, 1916 to 1927, there were only three years with
fewer than 204 rain-days, and the mean was as many as
214, or ten above the average. In other words, since 1916
we have had about 120 rain-days more than we ought to
have had, an accumulation of rainy weather which is unusual.
The year with fewest rain-days was 1887, which received
thirty less than the average number, so that in order to

restore the adverse balance of the last twelve years, four very dry years would be required.

The abnormal number of rain-days was especially noticeable during the summer of 1927, and even more than the heavy rainfall, made this season one of the most dismal in living memory, conspicuous even in the series of six consecutive wet summers. It was even referred to by the Chancellor of the Exchequer, who in the opening sentence of the Budget statement gave the epitome of the financial year as : " The road has lain continually uphill ; the weather has been wet and cheerless." The cricket season was memorable for the number of matches abandoned, often with less than six hours' play. The popular impression of the weather of the year was considerably influenced by the wet August Bank Holiday ; the amounts for that day were everywhere small, rarely exceeding half an inch, but in the south-east of England the rain was sufficient to prevent any outdoor recreation. In London it commenced to rain soon after nine in the morning, and continued with some short breaks until about seven in the evening, but the total fall was only about 0·3 inch. This affords a good illustration of the annoying manner in which a relatively small quantity of rain can ruin the possibilities of a public holiday.

The rainfall of August Bank Holiday was almost entirely confined to the south-east of a line from the Isle of Wight to the Wash. Elsewhere the day was mainly fine. It is not without interest to recall the distribution of fine weather during two subsequent public holidays. During Christmas, 1927, Londoners were again unfortunate, more favourable weather being experienced even in the English Lake District and the Western Highlands of Scotland. Easter, 1928, was, on the other hand, most favourable for London, which was one of the warmest parts of the country. The variability of the weather over the country is again demonstrated by the contrast in Ireland, where leaden skies or a downpour of rain replaced the glorious sunshine and refreshing breeze of other parts of the British Isles. In Ulster there was steady rain from morning to night, and nearly all the outdoor fixtures on the Easter Monday were ruined.

Real hot days during the summer of 1927 were few, and most of the newspapers revived the story of the American who on his return home had difficulty in remembering whether the summer in England occurred on a Tuesday or Wednesday. Apparently it was the type of weather D'Artagnan must have encountered during his more adventurous visits here, since he referred to England as a country " *où le soleil ressemble à la lune.* . . ."

The year was unusually prolific in meteorological peculiarities. It is usual for many stations to record each year long runs of little or no rain in the summer months, but we do not look for them after September. In 1927 the position was reversed : there was little continuous fine weather in summer, but a number of fine spells were recorded in autumn and winter, especially in the first half of October in South-West England, and again in the very dry December. The latter extended to the Western Highlands of Scotland, a region where rain usually falls on nearly every day in December. At Glenquoich, on Loch Quoich, the fall of half an inch for the month was only 3 per cent. of the average amount, and constituted not only the driest December on record there, but the driest month of any name. The average annual rainfall at this station is 110 inches, and less than 1 inch has been recorded in only three out of the 750 months' record ; in fact, in this rainy region a month with less than 1 inch is as rare as a completely rainless month in the south-east of England. The comparison between the weather of December in London and in the English Lake District was most striking, the actual fall of rain and snow during the month being three times as much in London as at Keswick. While Londoners experienced snowstorms on many days around Christmas, the days in Keswick were mostly bright and crisp. There was a return to a more normal rainfall distribution in January, 1928, when Keswick recorded rain on every day, giving a total of 12 inches compared with 3½ inches in London.

Just as spells of dry days are usually a feature of the summer months, so spells of consecutive days with rain are usually a feature of winter. In 1927, while the dry December naturally limited the number of wet spells in the winter, the number in the summer was unusually large. In this respect, as in so many others, summer gave place to winter and winter to summer, until the Christmas snowstorm came to restore the balance of the seasons.

The run of wet months from June to September was the most striking feature of the rainfall of the year. In association with the depression which had resulted from the stress of economic conditions, the effects of the wet summer fell with special severity upon the agriculturist. The year 1879 has often been quoted as a parallel case, and indeed we have to go back to that year before we find one with heavier and more persistent rain during these months. September was the wettest month of the year, although it was not as wet as September, 1918. In both months three times the average quantity of rain fell over considerable portions of England. Although the rainfall of July was the least striking over the country as a whole, locally it was extremely intense.

The main feature of the rainfall of July was the occurrence of intense thunderstorms, which were recorded somewhere in the British Isles on more than half the days during the month. During the night of the 6th to 7th more than one inch fell to the east of a line from the Wash to St. Leonards. At Deal and Dover there was as much as 3 inches. At Dover 2·3 inches fell during the night at the fairly uniform rate of half an inch an hour, so that persistent rather than especially torrential rain was the main feature of this storm, which was, however, one of the worst ever experienced at Dover. At times the streets were almost impassable and vivid lightning lit up the town. The rainfall of July 11th was much more terrific while it lasted. It was that of a typical summer afternoon thunderstorm. Rain commenced in the early afternoon and fell with such intensity that in a few hours about 3 inches was recorded in Kensington.

The rain was very local, for in the Strand, on Putney Common and at Sudbury, places only four miles to the east, four miles south and six miles north-west of Kensington, the falls were insignificant. As seen from Worthing, the cumulus clouds to the north during the afternoon were very impressive, while the South Downs and the coast from Beachy Head to the Isle of Wight were bathed in sunshine. In the late afternoon one massive cumulus cloud towered above all the others, its enormous thickness probably accounting for the intense darkness which prevailed in parts of London during this storm. The rainfall of the afternoon was similar to that of June 16th, 1917, both in general distribution and in the duration of the storm. On both occasions there was much damage by flooding in the low-lying districts, and the underground railways were disorganised.

The abnormally wet summer of 1927 was not confined to the British Isles, for Paris recorded the wettest summer since 1806, with the exception of that of 1854. June, July, August and September, 1927, were all wetter than usual, the fall of June and July together being twice the average. The amount of water discharged into the sea by the River Elbe during the year was considerably in excess of the average, especially during the early part of the year, the increase which commenced in 1926 continuing well into the middle of the next year, after which there was an appreciable fall off in the total flow of the river. The worst period of flooding came towards the end of April, when the Oder, Elbe and Havel were all over their banks. From then on to the end of November Europe was never entirely free from floods—in May in central Switzerland and Portugal ; June in Eastern Norway ; July in many widely separated localities ; August in Central Europe ; September in Poland, Northern Portugal, Eastern Spain, Switzerland, the upper Rhine valley, Austrian Tyrol and Northern Italy ; October in Bulgaria, Yugoslavia and Albania, and November in Northern France, Western Germany and again Switzerland. In parts of the Italian Alps landslides became a serious problem, and some villages are threatened with destruction by the

" moving mountain." In November also torrential rains caused the bursting of a dam in Western Algeria, flooding 900 square miles and drowning about 2,000 people. In December there was serious flooding in Northern Morocco, 1,800 square miles being under water.

All these flood reports from Europe, however, pale into insignificance before the disaster which befell the Mississippi Valley in the early months of the year. The Mississippi is confined to its channel by a series of artificial banks or levees, and as it bears great quantities of silt it has gradually been raising its bed. The levees have been raised in turn, until the river became a sort of elevated aqueduct, the upper surface of the water in time of flood being in places many feet above the level of the surrounding country. Already in December, 1926, some of the tributary streams were heavily flooded and an excessive rainfall in February, March and April, 1927, increased the volume of water pouring into the main stream. During April the whole Mississippi from Cairo to New Orleans rose relentlessly : the first levees gave way on the 17th and from then to the end of the month reports of further breaches or " crevasses " followed in rapid succession, as the sodden banks became too weak to withstand the pressure of the water, which in many places was already lapping over their summits. More than 18 million acres, or 28,573 square miles were flooded, equivalent to very nearly half the area of England and Wales. Owing to the gradual rise of the water the loss of life in river floods is not generally proportionate to the material damage ; on this occasion the death-roll was 214, but more than 600,000 persons were made homeless and the material loss is estimated at 284 million dollars, or more than 70 million pounds. Losses, both of life and property, would have been very much heavier but for the warnings issued by the Weather Bureau which predicted the height of the floods from one to four weeks in advance.

CHAPTER III

THE WET SUMMER OF 1924

" All the months of the year
Fear a fair Februeer."

THE year 1924 disputes with 1927 the doubtful honour of
including the most dismal of the series of dismal summers
which followed the remarkable drought and fine weather of
1921. 1924 was the more noteworthy not only because the
rainfall over the southern half of England and Wales was
very greatly in excess of the average, but also because of the
long run of consecutive wet months. Over the country as a
whole there were seven successive months, April to October,
each of which had more than its fair share of rainfall. So
long a run of wet months over the British Isles is unusual,
in fact it had not occurred since the remarkable run of
thirteen wet months from November, 1876, to November,
1877. In 1924, however, the effects of the long run were
minimised—except perhaps for holiday makers—by the
dryness of the two preceding months, February and March,
and by the occurrence of the heaviest rain at a time when
the evaporation is large and the streams and rivers are
usually at their lowest. Actually no February and March
together for the last sixty years were as dry as those months
in 1924. Much of the heavy rain of the late spring and early
summer was therefore absorbed by the dry ground, and
went to replenish the springs and rivers.

A peculiarity which 1924 shared with its predecessor 1923
was the abnormally heavy rainfall in the north-west of
Ireland and the west of Scotland, areas where usually the
rainfall does not vary greatly from year to year. In 1923,
and still more in 1924, however, these outlying regions

D

shared in the general excess of rainfall, and recorded the largest totals of the past sixty years.

Of the seven wet months from April to October, 1924, May and September stand out as the wettest. The rainfall of May exceeded that of every previous May since before 1870, while in the same period the rainfall of September was exceeded only three times, in 1885, 1896 and 1918. July was notable as a month of thunderstorms. On July 22nd thunderstorms occurred over several small areas between Midhurst in Sussex and Enfield to the north of London, as much as 4·07 inches being recorded at the Royal Horticultural Society's ground at Wisley. There was another violent storm in the north of London on July 29th, as a result of which Parliament Hill looked like the scene of a " cloudburst." At Hampstead, which was caught by both storms, the total for the month was 7·60 inches. Although we have records for London going back as far as 1774, this Hampstead total has only twice been exceeded—in October, 1880, when 8·81 inches were measured at Lee, and in July, 1918, when 8·31 inches fell at Bermondsey.

Over the whole summer period from April to September the distribution of rainfall is a characteristic example of the cyclonic type, as defined in the *Introduction*. Even in a season of cyclonic type the rainfall is not everywhere the same ; the effects of the configuration of the ground and of the local occurrence of thunderstorms can still be traced. The distribution of rainfall over the British Isles during this period of six months is shown in Fig. 4, and it is interesting to examine the map in detail and to note the relative extents of the orographic, cyclonic and thunderstorm types of distribution. The least rainfall during the period occurred in the Fen District, with 11 inches at Lincoln. The smaller rainfall of the " dry east coast " of Great Britain was well marked even in this wet summer. Apart from the area along the south-east and east coasts stretching from the Isle of Wight in the south to Thurso in the north, more than 20 inches was recorded practically everywhere. The fall increased towards the west, and more than 40 inches was

recorded over parts of the mountains of Wales, the English
Lake District, the Western Highlands of Scotland and the
mountains of Kerry, Connemara and Donegal. Some of
the largest totals are set out below :—

County	Station	Rainfall, April to September, 1924
		inches
Cumberland - -	Borrowdale (The Stye) - -	101·8
Carnarvon - -	Snowdon (Llyn Llydaw) -	95·4
Inverness - -	Loch Quoich (Loan) - -	62·3
Galway - -	Delphi Lodge - - -	58·5

The fall at Borrowdale in this one summer was more than
the total of four average years in London. The controlling
influence of the orography is therefore well marked, and it
is only when the map is examined in detail that we can
discover areas of heavy rainfall which fell on relatively low
ground, and were not due to the influence of the hills. In
the first place there is an area near Bridgwater which received
as much rain as either Exmoor, the Quantocks or the Mendips
in spite of the greater elevation of these areas. This was due
in the main to the intense thunderstorm rain of August 19th
near Bridgwater. At places in this region 220 per cent. of
the average summer rainfall was recorded compared with
150 per cent. on Exmoor and the Mendips. It is noticeable
that the areas affected by the less intense thunderstorm rains
of July are not apparent on the map. In general it is found
that thunderstorms produce so little rain compared with
that caused by a range of hills or mountains or by the passage
of barometric depressions across these islands, that the
thunderstorm type of distribution is rarely shown on rainfall
maps for a period greater than one month.

There was also a belt of relatively heavy rainfall stretching
from Lake Vyrnwy in Montgomeryshire (the source of much
of Liverpool's water-supply) to Eastbourne. At Worcester
and Malvern the fall exceeded 190 per cent. of the average.

The north-west of Ireland also received unusually heavy rainfall with 170 per cent. of the average at both Ballynahinch Castle in Connemara and Markree Observatory in Sligo. In both these areas the unusually heavy rainfall was

FIG. 4—RAINFALL (INCHES), APRIL–SEPTEMBER, 1924

associated with the passage of depressions across these islands. As is usually the case with rainfall maps covering a period of at least six months there is in general more rain on the mountains than on the plains, but here certain large areas have received additional rains which have fallen apparently on hill and valley alike. These areas are emphasised when a map showing the rainfall as a percentage of the average is considered, and it is from such maps that the classification into cyclonic and orographic is most readily made. If over most of the country the difference between the fall in the mountains and in the plains is more marked than usual, then the orographical type is highly developed, while if the difference is smaller than usual, with large excesses in low-lying areas, then the cyclonic type is taken as prevailing.

The summer of 1924 was distinguished by one of the heaviest falls of rain ever recorded in one day in the British Isles. The fall of 9·40 inches measured at Brymore House near Cannington, to the east of the Quantocks, on the morning of August 19th, is the second largest daily measurement on record. Curiously the largest also occurred in Somersetshire, at Bruton on June 28th, 1917, when 9·56 inches was recorded. Judging from the records of the last fifty years we have come to regard the southern half of England and Wales, with its large land surface, as more liable to intense thunderstorm rains than the remainder of the British Isles. Although statistical proof is wanting there is, however, little doubt that the rain which occasioned the Moray floods of 1829 (see Chapter XIII) was at least as intense as any of recent years, so that no area in the British Isles can be regarded as immune from the possible occurrence of a daily fall of ten inches. It is interesting to recall that when the observer at Cannington realised that he had to measure an abnormal fall, since the rain-gauge was full almost to overflowing, the rain-water being actually in the funnel itself, he called two other gardeners and arranged for a flower-pot to be put on a wall each time the measuring glass, holding half an inch, was filled. The measurement was also confirmed by the depth of rain-water which had accumulated in some cattle tubs and troughs. The next largest measurement was only 5·60 inches at Ashford House, but in view of the smaller amount of local damage at the latter place this can be regarded as confirming the larger fall. In fact the intense rain was so very local that it is fortunate that any measurement at all was available. At a distance of four miles to the south-west and three miles to the north-east of Brymore House the fall was only one inch, while 25 miles to the north there was no rain at all.

The heaviest precipitation occurred in the early morning of the 19th, when it is estimated that eight inches of rain and hail fell in five hours. The observer commented on the noise of the downpour, almost stifling that of the thunder, while the rain is described as falling in solid sheets as if being emptied from buckets. Apparently two or three thunder-storms followed each other in quick succession. It has been computed that in these few hours 2,000 million gallons of rain fell over an area of 44 square miles, enough water to meet London's requirements for eight days. In the Louth flood of May 29th, 1920, when 22 people were drowned, about 1,200 million gallons of rain fell in the valley of the Lud, draining to Louth, an area of 22 square miles. The fall in the Cannington storm was therefore rather greater than that at Louth, but the flooding and damage were by no means so marked. This was due to Cannington's natural advantages ; the area is drained by three separate streams, it is near the sea, and there are no steep slopes. Fortunately high water had passed before the rush of flood water, so that the river Parrett was able to cope with the abnormal run-off. This illustrates that the damage associated with heavy rain is dependent on local factors, and is naturally greatest when these factors operate together. An example of the way in which catastrophe can result from the com-bination of several causes, no one of which would be disastrous by itself, is seen in the Thames flood of January, 1928, described in Chapter VII.

It is difficult to assign the occurrence of the heavy rainfall at Cannington to any particular cause, as it was so local that it almost entirely escaped the network of stations reporting general climatological observations. The information avail-able suggests however that cold " polar " air from the Arctic was travelling eastward across the country, the lower layers being warmed up by contact with the heated ground, until the whole mass became unstable and marked instability rainfall resulted. The occurrence of thunder points to some upward motion of the air, but the hailstones, which lay on the ground in the morning to a depth of three to four inches, were generally small, so that there is no reason to suppose that violent upward currents were present such as are necessary for the formation of very large hailstones.

The summer of 1924 was the wettest for the last sixty years over a considerable part of the British Isles. The rainfall at stations representative of these areas, both in actual inches and as a percentage of the average summer rainfall, is set out below, together with the average.

County	Station	Summer Rainfall, April to September		
		Average	1924	
		inches	inches	per cent. of average
ENGLAND AND	WALES.			
Hereford -	Ross - - -	13·0	22·7	175
Shropshire -	Church Stretton -	14·9	27·1	182
Isle of Man	Douglas - - -	17·5	30·0	172
SCOTLAND.				
Perth - -	Blair Atholl - -	14·2	20·7	146
Aberdeen -	Aberdeen - -	14·5	24·2	167
IRELAND.				
Westmeath	Mullingar - -	17·4	25·6	147
Louth -	Greenore - -	15·6	24·1	155
Mayo -	Ballinrobe - -	20·3	30·7	151
Sligo - -	Markree Observatory	19·6	33·9	173
Armagh -	Armagh Observatory	16·0	23·4	146
Tyrone -	Omagh - - -	18·8	27 1	145

The summer was the wettest on record over three well defined areas, one to the east of the Welsh mountains, another between the Grampians and the coast of Aberdeen, and the third over the northern half of Ireland and the Isle of Man. These three areas include roughly one-fifth of the whole of the British Isles. The occurrence of the run of wet summers in 1923, 1924 and 1927 is all the more striking because the last run of outstanding wet summers occurred fifty years ago in the 'seventies. The years 1872, 1873, 1874, 1877, 1878 and 1879 all gave summers which were the wettest in the last sixty years in some part of the country. In fact the 'seventies gave the wettest summer over about two-thirds of the whole country. The summer of 1879 was the worst in the series over the whole of the southern half of England and Wales, as well as locally in the south-west of Scotland and the extreme south-east of Ireland. There is some consolation in recalling that in southern England at any rate the recent summers were not so wet as those which the previous generation had to endure, for the regions in which the summer of 1924 was the wettest on record were all in the more sparsely inhabited parts of these islands.

When we turn to the rainfall of the year 1924 as a whole, we find that stations representative of only about one-twentieth of the whole area recorded their largest fall in that year. For certain of these stations the fall in 1924 is set out below both in actual inches and as a percentage of the average.

County	Station	Average Annual Rainfall, 1881–1915	1924 (Wettest Year)	
			Amount	Per cent. of Average
ENGLAND.		inches	inches	
Wiltshire -	Salisbury Plain -	28·1	39·3	140
Devon, S.	Ashburton - -	51·8	71·6	138
Devon, S.	Sidmouth - -	32·4	44·3	137
Somerset -	Street - -	29·5	40·5	137
Gloucester	Fairford - -	25·6	37·4	146
IRELAND.				
King's Co.	Birr Castle - -	32.7	42·8	131
Mayo -	Ballinrobe - -	48·7	63·1	130
Sligo -	Markree Observatory.	43·5	59·3	136

The year 1924 was the wettest on record in parts of the

south-west of England and the north-west of Ireland (see Fig. 5). In these districts the rainfall was about 50 inches, which, being twice the average rainfall of London is a total much larger than any likely to be recorded in that

FIG 5.—ANNUAL RAINFALL 1868–1924. WETTEST YEAR

city. While these annual totals are very large in comparison with the amounts to which we are accustomed in south-east England, they do not begin to compare with those recorded practically every year in the English Lake District, Snowdonia and the Western Highlands of Scotland. In 1924 it was the

English Lake District which gave the largest total of rather more than 200 inches. This was recorded at the Stye at the head of Borrowdale in Cumberland. Even this large amount fell short of the largest annual totals on record for these islands. More than 240 inches was measured at the Stye in Cumberland in 1872 and 1923, at Ben Nevis Observatory in Inverness-shire in 1898 and at Llyn Llydaw on Snowdon in 1909. The largest measurement is that of 247·3 inches at the Stye in 1923. It should be borne in mind that strict comparison between the rainfalls of these three areas is not possible, because it is hardly likely that rain-gauges will be situated in the precise areas of the actual maximum falls. There is most information about the rainfall in the Lake District and Snowdonia, and there is little doubt that even in these localities no gauge has yet been set up in the actual place of maximum fall.

CHAPTER IV

1903—THE YEAR WITH TWO WET SPELLS

" For as the rain cometh down, and the snow from heaven, and returneth not thither."—ISAIAH LV. 10.

IN Dr. H. R. Mill's admirable paper on " The Three Wettest Years of British Rainfall," published in *British Rainfall*, 1903, a map of the distribution of rainfall during 1903 is included

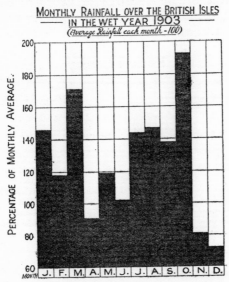

FIG. 6—MONTHLY RAINFALL OVER THE BRITISH ISLES IN THE WET YEAR 1903

along with those for 1872 and 1877. It is shown that over the British Isles generally only the former year was wetter than 1903. None of the subsequent twenty-five years have passed the high water mark of this year, and probably during the last 100 years the rainfalls only of the years 1872 and 1852 have exceeded that of 1903 over the British Isles as a whole. The rainfall of 1872 is dealt with in Chapter V, while some references to 1852 appear in Chapter VII.

Although 1903 was not the wettest year on record, it yet presents some features sufficiently noteworthy for mention. Chief among these was the occurrence of two spells of rain, one of them from January to March, typically orographical, and the second from May to October, typically cyclonic in its distribution. The monthly rainfall over the British Isles generally is shown in Fig. 6. Each of the months January to March was marked by large totals of rainfall in the mountainous districts of the west. The most striking contrast between the actual fall along the east coast and that in the west of Great Britain occurred in February. In the table below is given the rainfall for five of the driest and five of the wettest stations.

FEBRUARY, 1903

Low Rainfall			High Rainfall		
County	Station	Amount inches	County	Station	Amount inches
Norfolk	Geldeston -	0·1	Inverness -	Ben Nevis Observatory	36·2
Suffolk	Bury St. Edmunds	0·3	Cumberland	Borrowdale (The Stye)	27·7
,,	Aldborough-	0·3	,,	Ullscarf -	23·5
Norfolk	Brundall -	0·3	Westmorland	Mickleden -	22·4
Cambs.	Stretham -	0·4	Inverness -	Glenquoich	21·3

The average rainfall of 0·29 inch at the five dry stations in the east of England during February is little more than one-hundredth of the average of 26·23 inches at the five wet stations. The pressure map for the month shows a distribution typical of that usually associated with orographical rains. While the general trend of the isobars from west-south-west to east-north-east was in the same direction as usual, they were much closer together than they usually are, so that the pressure gradient was steeper. Normally in February the difference of pressure between the Shetlands and Eastbourne is 8½ millibars, but in February, 1903, the difference in pressure was as much as 24 millibars. There was a succession of strong south-west winds with frequent rain along the Atlantic seaboard, and exceptionally high temperatures. During the night of the 26th and 27th the wind reached gale force along the west coast, and on the Leven Viaduct, near Ulverston, a train consisting of ten passenger coaches and vans was overturned. In Ireland thousands of trees were uprooted and the gale was the worst since the night of the " big wind " on January 6th, 1839. February was also remarkable for the harmless but no less interesting fall of dust or " red rain " reported between the 21st and 23rd by observers over an area of 20,000 square miles in the southern half of England and Wales as well as in many countries on the Continent. It is estimated that in England and Wales alone the total quantity of dust was not less than 10 million tons. The dust was traced back to the Sahara and must have been carried by the wind for a distance of at least 2,000 miles in a wide sweep, around the peninsula of Spain and Portugal, probably crossing the Azores.

March, 1903, was not only the wettest month of the year, but the wettest March during the period of comparable statistics from 1870 to date. The prevalence of south-west and west winds continued and the month was exceptionally warm. While vegetation was unusually forward, the farm work was backward owing to the saturated condition of the ground. At many stations rain fell on every day of the month, while in the English Lake District and parts of the Western Highlands of Scotland the sequence exceeded the traditional " forty days " which figure in the superstitions of so many " Rain Saints." The wet period generally continued from February 19th to April 7th, a period of 48 days. So well defined an area with more than 40 rain days is most unusual, although considerably longer wet periods are on record at individual stations : for example, there were 89 days with rain from August 12th to November 8th, 1923, at Eallabus in the Isle of Islay.

The three months, January to March, presented the most unusual occurrence of 10 inches in each of the months at over one hundred stations in the British Isles. Such records were found in the English Lake District, Central and Northern Wales and in the Western Highlands of Scotland. At nearly all these stations more than one-third of the whole year's rainfall fell in the three months, even though it was a wet year. At Ben Nevis Observatory, in Inverness-shire, the totals for the three months were 34, 36 and 38 inches, respectively, giving a total of 108 inches, very nearly half of the year's total of 217 inches, which was itself unusually large. It is not without interest to recall that on February 11th a conference under the auspices of the Sanitary Institute was held to consider the shortage of water available for supply. This emphasises that although 1903 was a year of most unusually heavy rainfall it occurred in a run of dry years. During the twenty-two years, 1884 to 1905, as many as sixteen were drier than the average, and of the remaining six only 1903 was markedly wet.

The second wet spell lasted from May to October, 1903. Although during April the general rainfall over the British Isles was little short of the average, the month was conspicuous by contrast with the wet months which preceded and followed, and it formed a welcomed break between a wet winter and a wet summer. The distribution of the rainfall in May, June and July was of the cyclonic type, with large excesses in the southern half of England. May calls for little comment, but June was most remarkable. For about a fortnight round the middle of the month the west and north of the British Isles experienced exceptional dryness, while heavy rain fell almost daily over the southern and eastern parts of England. This distribution was caused by the passage of a series of slow and irregularly moving depressions immediately to the north or to the south of the English Channel. Subsequently under the influence of depressions passing across the north-western fringe of these islands a more normal distribution of rainfall was re-established, heavy rain falling in the west and none in the south-east. For the month as a whole the mean pressure presented the unusual feature of a complete reversal of the normal distribution, the highest values being in the north and the lowest along the English Channel. Over the British Isles generally the rainfall of June was 102 per cent., but on examining the distribution of the rainfall in this " on the whole average " month it appears that over England and Wales the general rainfall was 120 per cent. of the average and over Scotland and Ireland between 80 and 90 per cent. Even within the borders of England and Wales the irregularities were remarkable. In parts of Westmorland less than half the average rainfall was recorded, while over the lower part of the Thames Valley there was from three to four times the average amount. The contrast between the west of Ireland and the east of Essex in June, while not as striking as that between East Anglia and the English Lake District or the Western Highlands in February, is sufficiently abnormal to require special comment. A similar table is given for comparison.

JUNE, 1903

Low Rainfall			High Rainfall		
County	Station	Amount inch	County	Station	Amount inches
Sligo -	Markree Obsy. -	0·7	Surrey -	Carshalton -	8·9
Mayo -	Westport - -	0·8	Kent -	Hayes -	7·4
Donegal	Letterkenny -	0·9	Surrey -	Banstead -	7·0
Argyll -	Islay (Eallabus) -	0·9	Essex -	Epping -	7·0
Clare -	Miltown Malbay	1·0	Herts -	Broxbourne	6·8

In this case the east was about nine times wetter than the west. What makes the figures even more remarkable is that in most years the June rainfall in the west is much greater than in the east of the country, and June, 1903, represents a complete reversal of the usual conditions. It shows a state of affairs quite as unusual as the much larger difference quoted for February, when the wet stations were very wet and the dry stations particularly dry. One commonly thinks of the rain of June as mainly associated with thunderstorms, heavy rain storms affecting small and scattered areas and lasting only for a few hours, usually accompanied by great heat. In 1903 the wetness of June in the south of England was due to steady rain lasting for many hours at a time, unaccompanied by thunder except on rare occasions, and associated with exceptionally low temperature. The rain was, in fact, rather of an autumnal than a midsummer type.

The unusual character of the rainfall during June is emphasized by the trace from the self-recording gauge at Camden Square (London). There was absolutely unbroken rainfall from 1 p.m. on the 13th to 11.30 p.m. on the 15th, a duration of 58½ hours. This is not only the longest period of continuous rain recorded at Camden Square since an automatic gauge was installed there in 1881, but the longest on record for any part of the British Isles. It is a remarkable exception to the rule that persistent rainfall is usually associated with the winter months, and intense rains of shorter duration with the summer months. The autographic records at Camden Square show that while, during the period 1881 to 1915, the average durations of rain of the three winter months, December, January and February, have been 49 hours, 43 hours and 39 hours, respectively, the averages for the summer months, June, July and August, have been only 30 hours, 27 hours and 28 hours, even though the months of 1903 are included. The corresponding average rainfall of the three winter months is actually less than that of the three summer months, the totals being 5·9 inches, compared with 6·6 inches. The total duration of rainfall at Camden Square for June, 1903, was 102 hours, or more than three times the average, and this is the only month since the duration was first recorded in 1881 in which the duration has exceeded 100 hours. The fall of the 13th–15th June, 1903, stands out in sharp contrast with that of 23rd June, 1878. On the latter occasion 3·28 inches fell in 56 minutes, from 1.32 p.m. to 2.12 p.m. and from 2.46 p.m. to 3.2 p.m., during a terrific thunderstorm. June, 1878, with 6·71 inches, was the only other June in the series back to 1858 which was wetter in London than June, 1903, with 6·43 inches.

July was an unusually wet month all over the country. In the sixty years of comparable data there are, however, as many as ten wetter Julys, including those of the recent years, 1915, 1918, 1920 and 1924. One of the most striking features was the heavy fall in the neighbourhood of the Thames Estuary on the 23rd, when 4·41 inches was recorded at Dartford and 4·35 inches at Buckhurst Hill, to the south of Epping Forest. This was associated with a cyclonic centre which passed along the French coast of the Channel in a north-easterly direction, in much the same way as those of June.

The succession of rain-bearing depressions which swept our islands was continued in August, bringing weather of a most uncongenial type. For August, " wet and cold," was the burden of the remarks of observers from Land's End to John o' Groats and from Slea Head to Lowestoft. With the single exception of Felixstowe the temperature was everywhere below the average, as usually happens in a summer month of considerable cyclonic activity : the air movement was much more decided than usual, fresh and strong breezes being commonly experienced, with a prevalence of winds from the north-west, south-west and south.

While the rainfall of September was considerably in excess of the average over the country generally, that of October was even more remarkable. It was not only the wettest October in the series, but the third wettest month (in actual inches of rain) of any name, December, 1876, and December, 1914, being somewhat wetter. Falls exceeding 20 inches for the month were recorded at over thirty stations in the English Lake District, Central Wales, and parts of Argyll and Stirling. Some of the largest falls, with the percentage of the year's total, are set out herewith :

E

Station	County	October, 1903	Year 1903	October as per cent. of the year
Ullscarf - - -	Cumberland	35·0	174·3	20
Borrowdale (Stye) -	Cumberland	32·5	222.1	15
Mountain Ash - - (Clydach Reservoir)	Glamorgan -	22·0	99·7	22
Blaenau Festiniog -	Merioneth -	21·4	135·1	16
Mull (Bunesson) -	Argyll -	20·3	108·9	19

The rainfall of the whole period, May to October, 1903, with 146 per cent. of the average over the British Isles generally, was one of the wettest six months on record, being comparable with that of April to September, 1879, or April to September, 1924. The largest excesses occurred in the southern half of England and Wales. Over this region the fall generally exceeded 150 per cent. of the average, and reached twice the average in the neighbourhood of London.

For many years 1903 was regarded as the standard of heavy rain in this country. Its outstanding position in a series of years which were mainly dry naturally focussed attention upon it, while the much wetter year 1872 had been almost forgotten, until it was re-discovered by the modern technique of rainfall investigation; 1903, however, still remains the wettest in England of the past fifty years, and probably the third wettest of the past hundred.

CHAPTER V

THE RAINY SEASONS OF THE 'SEVENTIES

" their virtues
We write in water."
—*Henry VIII*, Act IV, Scene 2.

AMONG the beliefs which the Briton holds about the weather, there is none to which he clings more tenaciously than his belief that it is getting worse. He remembers the dry years of the 'nineties, but he seems to have forgotten entirely, even if he be old enough to have had a personal experience of them, the wet years of the 'seventies, by far the wettest decade on record in these islands. If we may complete the quotation which heads this chapter, while the events of the wet years are written in water, those of the sunny years are more appropriately written in brass. Yet the wet years were the more memorable. Of the twelve years from 1872 to 1883, inclusive, only two, 1873 and 1874, had a rainfall below normal over the whole of England, while 1872 was the wettest year on record, and 1877 ranks with 1903 as the second wettest at least since 1852. The year 1879, though not especially wet as a whole, included one of the wettest summers on record. The year 1872 resembled that of 1903, in that both occurred in a run of dry years. On the other hand, 1877 was the wettest year in a run of nine wet years from 1875 to 1883.

After the occurrence of the disastrous flood of January, 1928, in London it was recalled that with the single exception of 1894, the last occurrences of severe flooding in the Thames were in the 'seventies and early 'eighties. It is probable that this was caused as much by the indirect effect of the sequence of wet years in which the ground had become saturated as by the direct influence of the heavy rains at the time. Similarly, the flood of 1928 may have been due in part to the saturation of the ground following a series of wet years, giving a more rapid and complete run off into the Thames of the rain and snow of the previous Christmas than usually happens.

Sir Alexander Binnie has shown in his classical paper, " On Mean or Average Annual Rainfall, and the Fluctuations to Which it is Subject," that on the average the wettest ten years in any long record received about 11 per cent. more than the average of the whole period. The unusual wetness of the 'seventies is illustrated by the fact that this decade was wetter than the average by this amount over very nearly

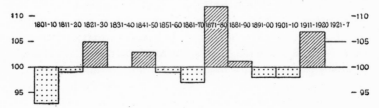

FIG. 7—VARIATIONS OF RAINFALL OVER ENGLAND BY DECADES

one-quarter of the total area of the British Isles. Considerable areas received more than 15 per cent. in excess. These areas included parts of the east coast of Great Britain, from Aberdeen to the Cheviots, from Middlesbrough to Hull, and to the South of the Fen District, as well as North Devon, South Wales, Shropshire and Staffordshire. Over the whole of England the excess during the decade 1871–80 averaged 12 per cent. (Fig. 7). At Marchmont House, to the north of the Cheviots, the fall during the 'seventies exceeded the average by 20 per cent. Actually the mean annual rainfall during the 'seventies at that station was 38·9 inches, whereas the average of a long period was only 32·2 inches. This illustrates that there may be a very large error in adopting the mean of a record of ten years as the long period average. Usually the average of at least thirty-five years is required.

The main peculiarity in the annual rainfall over the British Isles as a whole during the 'seventies was the return of well-

marked maxima at intervals of five years. This was a feature
of the rainfall from 1868, the earliest year for which comparable statistics are available, until 1882, and gave 1872,
1877 and 1882 as very wet years. Subsequently maxima
occurred at intervals of three years. This sequence held for
twenty-one years. No sooner, however, had the sequence
become sufficiently well established to receive comment than
a change occurred, giving a maximum at intervals of two
years. This continued until the famous dry year 1921, after
which the sequence has apparently reverted to the type
having a maximum every three years. Each of these four
types persisted just long enough to receive some publicity.
In 1906 Dr. H. R. Mill gave a warning that, "As a sequence of
one wet and two relatively dry years does not seem to have held
good before 1889, it is only reasonable to expect that it will
cease to hold good some time in the future." The warning
was timely, for the sequence was repeated only once again.

The distribution shown by the annual maps of the 'seventies was that in which the excesses were most marked in the
east of Great Britain. It is curious that the four stages already
referred to with maxima at intervals of five, three, two and
three years, respectively, roughly correspond with periods in
which the preponderating types of distribution were marked
by concentration of high rainfall in the east, west, south and
north-west, respectively. When the maxima were at the
longest intervals apart, as in the 'seventies, we have seen
that some of the wettest years were recorded.

The most striking months of 1872 were January and
June. The rainfall of January over the British Isles as a
whole was exceeded only by that of the Januarys of 1877
and the more recent 1928, the latter being the wettest January
ever recorded. June, 1872, was exceeded only by June, 1879,
although June, 1917, was nearly as wet. The rainfall of the
individual months of 1872 over the British Isles generally
exceeded the average in every month except August. The
only other year on record with so many wet months was
1877, while there were nine wet months in 1903 and again
in 1927, the wettest of recent years.

Not only was the rainfall of 1872 heavy and persistent ; it was also exceptionally widespread, exceeding the average over the whole of the British Isles. Since 1868 this has happened in only one other year, 1903, but the other excessively wet year, 1877, was very nearly in the same position. During the last sixty years the rainfall of some part of the British Isles has exceeded one and a half times the average amount in eleven different years, and then usually at only a few isolated stations. In 1872 the wet areas were so widespread that more than this amount was recorded over about one-third of the whole country. Although the most important areas of large excesses occurred in a broad belt along the east coast of Great Britain from Aberdeenshire to the mouth of the Humber, the type of distribution most common in the 'seventies, large areas in the Midlands, Wales and the southeast of Ireland also received more than one and a half times the average.

The year 1872 gave the largest annual fall in the last sixty years at stations representative of nearly half the whole area of the British Isles. These areas are shown in Fig. 5. They occur along the east coast of Great Britain, from the Moray Firth to Selsey Bill, over the Midlands and most of the western half of England and Wales, from Land's End to Southport, and in the south and north-east of Ireland. 1903 was the wettest year at stations representative of a fifth of the whole country, while either 1877, 1923 or 1924 was the wettest year over another fifth. These five years therefore accounted for the largest totals on record over 90 per cent. of the British Isles. In the case of the record at Kendal, in Westmorland, extending back to 1810, and at Ross, in Herefordshire, back to 1818, the wettest year was 1872. The areas with more than 150 inches of rainfall during 1872 were well developed in the English Lake District, Snowdonia and the Western Highlands of Scotland, while at the head of Borrowdale rather more than 240 inches was recorded—as much as Londoners expect to receive in ten years.

In comparison with 1872, the year 1877 is much less remarkable. 1877 gave the largest annual total in the last sixty years at stations representative of rather less than 10 per cent. of the whole British Isles. Such stations occurred mainly in parts of Central and Southern Scotland. One of the striking features of the distribution of the rainfall during 1877 was the marked similarity with 1872 of the positions of the areas with large excesses, but in 1877 the values were generally smaller. Falls of more than one and a half times the average occurred in three well-marked patches, the neighbourhood of Montrose, the Southern Uplands of Scotland and Anglesey. The distribution of the largest excesses along the east coast was not as well marked in 1877 as in 1872, 1876 or 1879, there being a superimposed tendency for the largest excesses to occur in a central belt across the British Isles, from the south-west to the north-east.

October, 1877, is remembered in Skye for unprecedented floods. Although rain falls more frequently in this island than in most other parts of the British Isles, intense falls are relatively infrequent, but on October 13th the rain was so intense that sluggish streamlets became raging torrents, and landslides carried down hundreds of tons of earth.

The years 1876 and 1877 gave the longest series of wet months on record. From September, 1876, to November, 1877, the rainfall of each month over the British Isles as a whole reached or exceeded the average. Omitting October, 1876, with only an average fall, we have a series of thirteen consecutive wet months. According to a recent investigation this long run included some of the wettest months ever recorded in the British Isles. Some details are given below :

Monthly Rainfall, 1870 to 1927	General Rainfall over the British Isles
	inches
Wettest month, December, 1876 - - -	8·9
Wettest two consecutive months, December, 1876, to January, 1877 - - - -	16·1
Wettest three consecutive months, November, 1876, to January, 1877 - - - -	21·0
Wettest four consecutive months, October, 1876, to January, 1877 - - - -	25·2

In the wettest month on record, December, 1876, there was more rain over the British Isles than usually falls in the three driest months of the year, April, May and June, while in the four wettest months, October, 1876, to January, 1877, there was as much as usually falls in the first eight months of the year. Such heavy rain in winter is harmful to crops, chiefly because it washes the soluble nitrates out of the soil. In a paper on *The Influence of Rainfall on the Yield of Wheat at Rothamsted*, Mr. R. A. Fisher showed that an excess of rainfall is least harmful in October, presumably because there is still ample time for the ground to make good its losses before the time of growth. There is a period centred in January in which dry conditions appear to be particularly desirable. At this time of the year each additional inch of rain costs from one to two bushels per acre in the wheat crop, but the effect is less on unmanured plots. Later in the year the effect of rain on growing plants is more complicated, for while rain supplies fully aerated water, saturation of the soil doubtless hinders root development.

In 1879 each of the six summer months April to September was considerably wetter than usual over the British Isles as a whole, while June was the wettest June on record. July, August and September each gave very nearly one and a half times the average fall over the country. August was remarkable for a severe thunderstorm at the beginning of the month, accompanied by hail which caused considerable damage at Kew Gardens, where most of the houses were subsequently closed to the public in order to avoid accidents from falling glass. The total cost of the repairs was estimated at £2,000. The rainfall at Nantlys in Flint, later in the month, was more persistent, a total of 6·36 inches falling almost without a break between noon on the 16th and midnight on the 17th. This is as much as is usually recorded there in the three months, April, May and June. The summer of 1879 was the wettest summer on record over most of the southern half of England and Wales, in the south-east of Ireland, and over considerable areas in the south-east of Scotland and along the north coast of Ireland.

At Camden Square, London, the fall of these six months amounted to 23·9 inches—only 0·6 inch short of the average for the whole year.

A good illustration of the compensation which nature provides sooner or later as a set-off against her prodigality is afforded by the remarkably dry winter of 1879 to 1880, which followed one of the wettest summers on record. The winter of 1879 to 1880 was the driest on record at stations representative of about three-quarters of the British Isles. In many places, therefore, the wettest summer on record was followed by the driest winter. For a number of stations where these two extremes occurred consecutively, the actual amounts are given together with the corresponding averages :

Station	County	Summer April–September		Winter October–March	
		1879	Per cent. of Average	1879–80	Per cent. of Average
		inches	per cent.	inches	per cent.
Camden Square -	London -	23·9	204	5·8	46
Tenterden - -	Kent -	19·2	165	6·4	40
Ventnor - - -	Hants -	22·8	195	7·2	42
Oxford - - -	Oxford -	20·9	173	6·3	50
Wellingborough -	Northants -	20·1	168	7·4	61
Bury St. Edmunds -	Suffolk -	21·3	170	5·5	44
Marlborough - -	Wilts -	23·8	179	6·0	35
Ashburton - -	Devon -	35·4	195	18·0	54
St. Austell - -	Cornwall -	30·6	170	13·6	49
Cardiff - - -	Glamorgan -	30·7	170	11·6	48
Haverfordwest -	Pembroke -	30·2	161	14·4	52
Girvan - - -	Ayr - -	30·0	145	19·2	66
Waterford - -	Waterford -	23·8	137	12·2	55
Buncrana - -	Donegal -	24·7	132	12·7	57

The failure of the harvest in 1879 cannot be attributed entirely to the excessive rainfall of the summer, for the spring was also unseasonable. Mr. Edward Fitzgerald wrote on May 18th, 1879, from Woodbridge, Suffolk :

" If your Winter has been such as ours ! And not over yet, as scarce a leaf on the trees, and a N.E. wind blowing cold, cough, bronchitis, etc., and the confounded Bell of a neighbouring Church announcing a Death day after day. I certainly never remember so long, and so mortal a Winter, among young as well as old."

We have said that, as far as human recollections are concerned, the wet years of the 'seventies are " writ in water." In another sense, however, they are writ in wood, for some measurements of the annual rings of tree growth in the Forest of Dean, made by Mr. E. G. Burtt and described in the *Meteorological Magazine* for March, 1928, have shown that, in this locality at least, trees grow most rapidly in dry weather and least rapidly when the soil is in a waterlogged condition after some years of heavy rain. The best record available is given by a yew tree which was cut in the winter of 1922–23, and was found to be 200 years old. This tree showed four periods of most rapid growth, about 1790, 1830, 1860 to 1870, and 1900, separated by three intervals when the annual rings were small. A comparison of the tree-growth measurements with annual rainfalls showed that the growth in any one year depended on the total rainfall of the preceding ten years, being greatest when this rainfall was least. From 1876 to 1885, following on the wet years of the 'seventies, the yew tree increased its diameter by little more than three-quarters of an inch, the smallest increase measured during the whole period between 1750, when the tree attained its mature rate of growth, and 1906, when it slackened through old age. The most rapid rate of growth in recent years occurred in 1906–15, following the relatively dry weather of the closing decade of the nineteenth century.

CHAPTER VI

HISTORIC RAINS

" A great deal of weather, all bad."—WALPOLE

WHEN we go back beyond the earliest measurements of rainfall in this country, we have to rely on the more or less vague descriptions of diarists and annalists. There is, for example, quite a lot of information about the weather in Pepys' Diary, while for the Middle Ages there is much material in the Anglo-Saxon Chronicle. After about 1651 we have sufficient information to construct a fairly continuous history of the weather in this country, and we are even able to make rough estimates of the actual amount of rainfall over the whole of England year by year, which are about as near the mark as if we had rainfall measurements from a single place and accepted that as representative of the whole country. Before 1650 our material is more scanty, and from the earlier centuries of the Christian era we have references only to the great floods or droughts which occur perhaps once in a generation or two or three times in a century. Some of these entries are sufficiently striking to be worth recalling ; those which are given here have been extracted mainly from a valuable MS. collection of quotations from the Anglo-Saxon Chronicle and Holinshed's Chronicle, by Eleanor A. Ormerod, now in the library of the Royal Meteorological Society ; from an article on " The November Floods of 1894 in the Thames Valley," by G. J. Symons and G. Chatterton (*Quarterly Journal of the Royal Meteorological Society*, Vol. XXI, 1895, p. 189), which also gives particulars of many earlier floods ; E. J. Lowe's well-known work on " Natural Phenomena and Chronology of the Seasons " (London, 1870) ; Sir Richard Gregory's Presidential Address to the Geographical Association in 1924, on " British Climate in Historic Times," also contains a great deal of information.

In the early records on which the following notes are ultimately based, it is sometimes difficult to discover the exact year in which any particular phenomenon occurred. A drought or wet period which extended from the end of one year to the beginning of the next may in course of time get entered to both years, and any special phenomena such as violent thunderstorms may be referred to the same dates in each year. Further complications were introduced by the change of the calendar in 1752, when eleven days were added to the date, and by the habit of some of the early chroniclers of ending the year on March 31st instead of December 31st. There may be occasional errors in the following dates due to these causes.

It is very difficult to form an opinion as to the amount of credence which should be placed in the sensational reports of the early chroniclers. The only detailed and reliable weather journal which has come down to us from the Middle Ages, was that kept by the Reverend William Merle at Oxford from 1337 to 1344. This journal, which was translated and published by G. J. Symons in 1891, presents a picture which is extraordinarily like that given by day-to-day records of recent years. The winters, sometimes mild and open, sometimes broken by short spells of frost ; the summers with a few days of moderate rain alternating with short intervals of golden weather ; nothing to remind us that we are reading of the fourteenth century instead of the twentieth.

The Thames flood of A.D. 9, the first on record in this country, was very likely a tidal affair, similar to that of January, 1928, which will be discussed in the next chapter. One wonders how the memory of such an early happening came to be preserved ; possibly the news crossed the Channel to Gaul and so came to the Romans. The flood of A.D. 48, however, may have been due to rainfall, when " the Thames overflowed, the waters extended through four counties, 10,000 persons were drowned, and much property was destroyed." A.D. 353 : " A great flood in Cheshire, 5,000

persons and an innumerable quantity of cattle perished."
These large death-rolls in round numbers are frequently
reported for early floods ; in the tidal floods described in the
next chapter they are frequently assessed as 100,000. As
the whole population of England at the time was perhaps
three or four million, such losses of life are obviously im-
probable, and they must be taken merely as signifying " a
large number," which there was no exact means of counting,
and which naturally grew as the reports spread.

One of the legends of St. Swithin relates that on July 15th,
971, the day appointed for the removal of the saint's remains
from the churchyard at Winchester to a splendid tomb
within the cathedral, he manifested his displeasure at the
disturbance by sending a great storm of rain, followed by
forty wet days. No contemporary writers mention this
storm, however, and it seems probable that it is a later
invention, to account for the well-known weather proverb
which had somehow become associated with the name of
St. Swithin.

There are no further entries of any importance referring
to floods in England until 1041, when according to the
Anglo-Saxon Chronicle : " All this year it was very sad in
many things, both in bad weather and earth-fruits."

In the latter half of the eleventh century we begin to
notice a tendency for wet years to occur in groups. Thus
between 1087 and 1124 we have records of great rains in
1087, 1093, 1097 and 1098, floods in 1099 and 1100, and
further great rains in 1103, 1105, 1116, 1117 and 1124 :

1087—" Through the great tempests there came a very great
famine."—*A. S. Chronicle*.

1093—" There was such a great deluge of rain, so great a season
of rain, as no one remembers before."—*Gregory*.
R. Bentley (" Weather in War-time," *Quarterly Journal*,
Vol. XXXIII, 1907, p. 83) states that when the Scots
who had invaded Northumberland in this winter were
defeated near Alnwick, the floods in the valleys barred
their retirement, and large numbers were killed.

1097—" This was in all things a very sad year, and over grievous
from the tempests."—*A. S. Chronicle*.

1098—" Great rains ceased not all through the year."—*A. S.
Chronicle*.

1116—" Excessive rains came immediately before August and greatly troubled and afflicted people until February 2nd."—*A. S. Chronicle.*

1117—" This was a very deficient year in corn, through the rains that ceased not almost all the year."—*A. S. Chronicle.*

1193—" Unusual storms, floods of waters, fearful and wintry thunderstorms throughout the whole of this year."— *Gregory.*

1200—" Springtime a great glutting and continual rain. . . . Wonderful tempests . . . and abundance of rain; meadows and marsh grounds quite overflowed and great quantity of corn and hay lost and carried away."

1202—" About this year great rains caused floods throughout the whole world."—*Gregory.*

1228—" Great thunders during most of the summer. Harvest sore hindered by continual rain."

1233—" Thunderstorms in England for fifteen successive days, with great rains and gales." " A marvellous wet summer, with many floods."

1236 was a year of extremes of rainfall. In January, February and part of March there were such floods of rain as no one remembered to have seen before. It rained for eight days without ceasing. " After a winter beyond measure rainy a constant drought attended by almost unendurable heat succeeded." (*See* page 152).

1239—" In the four months preceding Easter the flooding rain clouds did not cease."—*Gregory.*

1240 or 1242—" Rain continued for many days together, that rivers rose on marvellous heights, and the Thames . . . drowned all the country for the space of six miles about Lambeth."

1256—Towards the close of the year the " rivers were filled with abundance of water by reason of the great continual rain that marvellous floods followed thereupon."

1257 and 1258 also appear to have been years of unfortunate weather, the details of which are given by Sir Richard Gregory. Of the former year it is recorded that there were continuous rains in summer and autumn. The winter was exceptionally mild—" not a single frost or fine day occurred nor was the surface of the lake hardened by frost, but uninterrupted heavy falls of rain and mist obscured the sky until Purification (February 2)."—(Gregory.) Then followed a long spell of cold, dry, northerly winds, which persisted throughout April, May and the greater part of June, so that in the latter month

> " Scarcely were there visible any shooting buds of flowers. Many thousand human beings died of hunger."—
> *Gregory.*

Such corn as survived this inclement weather was almost destroyed by the excessive rain which came immediately after harvest ; and the chronicle ends with a great storm, accompanied by thunder and torrential rain, on December 1st. There followed a break with only two isolated wet seasons until 1283, when :—

> " all the summer and a great part of the autumn vehemently and continually rainy."—*Gregory.*
>
> 1287—" In the winter great floods by reason of the exceeding abundance of rain."
>
> 1290—" This year were frequently inundations of rain and especially in summer and autumn."—*Gregory.*

1315.—During the summer and autumn there was a great deal of heavy rain, so that the harvest was almost completely spoiled and famine resulted. People were reduced to eating horses and dogs. In 1327 there was another famine attributed to very wet weather.

> 1330—There was " exceeding great rain from the middle of May to the middle of October." " so violent that the harvest did not begin till Michaelmas."

In 1335 the corn was again spoiled by the heavy rain, and a famine resulted.

1348.—There were great rains, which continued from June 24th until Christmas, so that there was not one day or night dry together, by reason whereof great floods ensued.

> 1358—" Rivers and other waters rose on such heights through abundance of rain that fell in the latter end of harvest . . . many houses and towns were borne down and destroyed."

In 1365 the rain was again very violent, especially in the time of the hay harvest.

> 1369—" The corn was greatly damaged by floods."—*Gregory.*

1370—" Great wet and rain fell this year in more abundance than had been accustomed, much corn was lost."

1427.—It rained almost continually from Easter to Michaelmas, and the hay and corn harvests were greatly hindered.

1439.—Great tempests, raging winds and rain, great scarcity.

1483.—According to Bentley, this was another instance of the effect of the weather upon the course of battles :

> " In a premature attempt to seize the crown of England, Henry the Seventh's standard was hoisted by the Duke of Buckingham at Brecon in October, 1483. Owing to the elements, after a ten days' struggle the attempt failed. Through heavy rain that autumn both the Wye and the Severn were so deep in flood . . . that Buckingham was cut off from his allies in the Midlands. . . . This downpour and flood was long remembered as ' the Duke of Buckingham's Water.' "

1527 and 1528.—Two very wet years. In the spring of 1527 almost incessant deluges of rain prevented the corn from being sown. It rained almost continually in June, July and September, after which followed a scarcity so that many died for want of bread. There was further heavy rain in November and December, and by the middle of January there were great floods in the rivers. This was mercifully followed by a dry spell until April 12th, 1528, after which " it rained every day or night till June 3rd and in May it rained thirty hours continually, which caused great floods."

> 1542—" Intemperate wet summer."
> 1555—On September 21st, " by occasion of great wind and rain that had fallen was such great floods that the King's palace at Westminster and Westminster Hall was overflown with water."

1565.—On New Year's Eve the ice on the rivers was so thick that football was played on the Thames. Then on the night of January 3rd, 1565, it began to thaw, and on the 5th the ice had disappeared. This sudden thaw caused great floods, and many people were drowned, especially in Yorkshire.

1579 was another year of extremes. The troubles began

on February 4th, with snow which in London was two feet
deep in the shallowest places. It snowed until the 8th, then
followed a hard frost until the 10th, after which came a thaw
with continuous rain for a long time, which caused high
waters and great floods. On April 24th came more snow,
which lay a foot deep in London. In September and October
were " great winds and raging floods in sundry places,"
October being credited in the " Fugger News Letters " with
" fearful rough weather with rain, heavy snow and unusual
cold, such as has not been experienced for sixty years."

1594 was an unusually wet and unseasonable summer.
This is believed to be the year referred to in " A Midsummer
Night's Dream," Act II, Scene 1 :

> " Therefore the winds, piping to us in vain
> As in revenge, have suck'd up from the sea
> Contagious fogs, which, falling on the land
> Have every pelting river made so proud
> That they have overborne their continents :
> The ox hath therefore stretched his yoke in vain,
> The ploughman lost his sweat ; and the green corn
> Hath rotted ere his youth attained a beard :
> The folds stand empty in the drowned field
> And crows are fatted with the murrain flock ;
> The nine men's morris is filled up with mud. . . ."

1597.—We may refer to the " Fugger News Letters "
again :

January : " The rain lasts day and night, and the country
is waterlogged."

Readers will no doubt recall that the House of Fugger
was a great banking family with head-quarters in Germany,
and branches spread over the whole of Europe. Correspon-
dents in various countries sent regular reports of all happenings of interest which came to their notice, and these
voluminous reports were happily preserved. English editions
have been published by The Bodley Head, and give a wonderful picture of the life of the time. It is curious, however,
that in an agricultural age there are very few references to
abnormal seasons; perhaps the seasons were not particularly

F

extreme, but it is more probable that in the stirring Eliza-
bethan times there were sufficient sensational items of news
to occupy the writers without recourse to the weather.

> 1600—A geographical accident : " The River Trent, during a
> heavy flood, changed its course near the village of
> Holme, by Newark, through which means the town-
> ship became situated on the east side of the river
> instead of the west."—*Lowe.*
> 1648, according to Evelyn, " was a most exceeding wet year,
> neither frost nor snow all the winter for more than
> six days in all." This was followed by " a prodigously
> wet summer, very cold."

This was an unfortunate summer for the Isle of Wight,
not usually noted for its adverse weather :

> " This Sommer of the Kinges beinge here 1648 : wase more
> like winter then Sommer, for his Matie asked me wheather that
> weather wase usual in our Island I tolde him this 40 years I
> never knew the like before, wee had scarse 3 drie dayes togeather
> but rayne hygh windes & stormes. In Awgust we had not one
> drye daye, so that the corne wase like to rotte in ye ground."
> —*Meteorological Magazine*, 1925, p. 138.

1663 is described by Pepys : About May 8th there was a
violent thunderstorm at Northampton,

> " which caused extraordinary floods in a few hours, bearing
> away bridges, drowning horses, men and cattle. Two men
> passing over a bridge on horseback, the arches before and
> behind them were borne away, and that left which they were
> upon. . . . Stacks of faggots carried as high as a steeple, and
> other dreadful things. . . ."
> June 26th : " it is said there hath not been one fair day these
> three months, and I think it is true."
> On July 21st Parliament kept a fast for the unseasonable weather,
> but apparently with little effect, for on August 28th
> the diarist remarks that there has been " no summer
> at all, almost."

1682 was noteworthy for a flood in the Thames which is
omitted from the compilation by Symons and Chatterton.
Under the date 22nd April, Evelyn records : " This season
unusually wet, with rain and thunder," and " The Rector's
Book of Clayworth, Notts " (Nottingham, 1910) contains
the entry :

"Fro' ye middle of April to ye middle of May it was very wett : the meadows were generally drownd."

The floods in the Thames did much damage at Brentford, and their effects in London may be illustrated by the following quotation from the "Rutland Papers" (Mr. R. T. Gunther, in *The Times* for January 16th, 1928) :

"Never was such flodds known as has bine here, howses drowned and pore children drowne in theare cradels swimen up Fleet Bridge [the Fleet was then a navigable river], and there taken up, and tables and hogeds full of beare and all washed away, and peoppele geting up to theare uper lofts and hole heards of hogs drowned."

Were any of these years rainier than the wettest years which our "oldest inhabitants" can remember, 1852 and 1872 ? It is impossible to say, though, of course, as a matter of arithmetic, the odds are eighteen to one that eighteen centuries produced a year as wet as, or wetter than, one single century. A study of the figures of rainfall over England for the past two hundred years, however, shows that while a year as wet as 1852 might be expected on an average about once a century, 1872 was so outstanding that under general meteorological conditions similar to the present it is not likely to have been exceeded more than two or three times in the past fifteen hundred years. On the other hand, over England as a whole, the drought of 1921 does not seem to have been really phenomenal, and there may quite well have been many drier years since historical records began. This conclusion, based on purely statistical arguments, accords well enough with the historical evidence, for there is no single year which we can pick out from the descriptions as probably wetter than 1872, but as we shall see in Chapter XII, there are several years which leave on the mind an impression of greater drought than 1921. The group of years from 1087 to 1117 appears to have been abnormally wet, and may have rivalled the period from 1872 to 1886, which was the wettest of the past century, but we have not sufficient details to enable us to pick out any one year as the worst. 1258 appears to have been very wet, reminding us strongly of 1924, but as in the latter year the effect of the rains of the latter half of June and of July must have been greatly mitigated by the great dryness of the preceding months. Another point of similarity is that the preceding years, 1257 and 1923, were also wet.

1527 may have been even worse than 1258, when we consider its records of " deluges " in spring and of exceptionally heavy rain in June, July, September, November and December. Taking the two years 1527 and 1528 together, one would say that they have strong claims to the record of being rainier than any other pair of consecutive years since records began. 1648 is the next year to claim our attention, but judicially weighing the evidence, we must consider that its claims are not so circumstantial and convincing as those of 1258 and 1527.

In 1677 the earliest known rainfall record in this country commences, that of Townley in Lancashire, and we are better able to make comparisons with recent years. It is curious, however, that soon after the beginning of systematic rainfall observations a prolonged period of unusually dry weather set in, and in the hundred and fifty years between 1677 and 1826 there seems to have been no year which equalled 1872. The nearest approach was in 1768, which was much less wet than 1872, but only very slightly below 1852. In 1768 there was heavy rainfall and flooding in February, but the spring was dry and cold. Summer was dismal enough, but the heaviest rainfall came in the autumn, especially at the end of November, and according to Symons and Chatterton, on December 1st the Thames reached a flood level higher than any in the preceding years. " The Kennet and Loddon overflowed their banks. Burfield Bridge and part of Twyford Bridge were washed away and the Isis at Oxford rose 1 ft. 6 in. above any existing high water mark. The Exeter coach, with six passengers and four horses, was carried away by the flood near Staines, and all were drowned." On the whole, however, the flooding was not so severe as that in 1852. The floods of 1894 were even greater than those of 1852, and in parts of the river the water rose to a level a foot higher than any previously recorded. The year 1768 was no doubt the more noticeable at the time because the halcyon years of the first half of the eighteenth century, described in Chapter XI, would still have been fresh in men's memories. 1768 was, in fact, the first of a long spell of wet years, which continued until 1775, six of these eight years having a rainfall above the standard normal. This wet period considerably raised the water table of the chalk hills, and in 1774 Gilbert White wrote : " The land springs, which are called levants, break out much on the downs of Sussex, Hampshire and Wiltshire. . . . Land springs have never obtained more since the memory of man than during that period [the past ten or eleven years]. . . . Such a run of wet seasons, a century or two ago, would, I am persuaded, have occasioned a famine."

CHAPTER VII

THE THAMES FLOOD OF 1928, AND OTHER FLOODS

" Things will work to ends the slaves o' the world
Do never dream of."
—WORDSWORTH

IN the preceding chapters we have been dealing with heavy rains which sometimes raised the levels of the rivers to such an extent as to result in destructive floods. On streams and rivers which run rapidly off high ground such floods sometimes rise suddenly and may cause loss of life, but on the larger rivers near the sea they usually set in more slowly, and give the occupants of the threatened regions time enough to save themselves, if not their household goods. In tidal waters such as the lower parts of the Thames the most disastrous floods are not due entirely or even mainly to heavy rainfall, though the latter not infrequently plays a part ; they are caused instead by a combination of circumstances, among which spring tides and strong winds play the leading rôles.

The greater part of the rise of water level in such floods as the fatal visitation in London on January 7th, 1928, is of course due to the tide. This book is not the place to go in detail into the astronomical causes of tides ; it is sufficient to recall that the difference between high and low water, and the level of high water, are greatest two or three days after new and full moon, giving *spring* tides. To explain how weather conditions may sometimes exaggerate the height of spring tides, however, it is necessary to add a few words about the way in which the tidal currents reach the Thames Estuary. The tidal wave advancing from the Atlantic towards the British Isles divides into two, one wave passing into the North Sea round the north of Scotland, and the other travelling up the English Channel. The Straits of Dover are, however, so narrow that the Channel wave probably has little effect on the tides in the Thames Estuary, which are thus mainly due to a tidal stream advancing southwards down the North Sea.

Anyone who has watched the waves raised by the wind will readily understand that the wind drives some of the surface water of the sea in front of it, and when the wind blows a gale the amount of water driven along in this way may be very great. Actually the water is driven, not straight forward, but to the right of the wind, so that a north-westerly wind, for example, will drive the water towards the south or south-west, the exact direction depending on the persistence and violence of the wind, the depth of the sea, and the direction of the tidal stream. The most favourable wind for an unusually high tide in the Thames Estuary appears to be a northerly or north-westerly gale off the coast of Scotland, which drives a large quantity of water into the southern or south-eastern part of the North Sea. If at the same time, as not infrequently happens, a south-westerly gale is blowing in the English Channel, some of the water from the Channel will also be driven into the North Sea, but the Straits of Dover are so narrow that this contribution must be comparatively unimportant.

The effect of north-westerly gales in the North Sea has been known for a long time, for the Rev. W. Derham, F.R.S., in a contribution to Defoe's history of the Great Storm of 1703, wrote :

" Another unhappy Circumstance with which this Disaster was join'd, was a prodigious Tide, which happen'd the next Day but one, and was occasion'd by the Fury of the Winds ; which is also a Demonstration, that the Winds veer'd for Part of the Time to the Northward : and as it is observable, and known by all that understand our Sea Affairs, that a North West Wind makes the Highest Tide, so this blowing to the Northward, and that with such unusual Violence, brought up the Sea raging in such a manner that in some Parts of *England* 'twas incredible, the Water rising Six or Eight Foot higher than it was ever known to do in the Memory of Man."

There is another possible complication in the effect of the winds, and that is the power of a strong east wind to drive the water of the rising tide rapidly into the narrowing estuary of the Thames. Fortunately this climax very rarely occurs in conjunction with the other factors making for a tidal flood, but an easterly wind occurred for a time during the great flood of January 2nd, 1877, and undoubtedly increased the height of the water.

There is another factor. Gales are proverbially associated with a low barometer ; and when the barometer is low over any part of the ocean, the level of the water tends to rise there above that at places where the barometer is high. The level of the mercury measures the downward pressure of the air, and if this pressure is unequal in two different places, the greater pressure must create a dimple in the sea, while the water bulges up into the air where the pressure is least. Mercury is about thirteen times as heavy as water, and a difference of an inch in the level of the barometer causes a difference of thirteen inches in the level of the sea. These variations of barometric pressure can only cause relatively small fluctuations in the height of the tides, but, coming on top of a spring tide already augmented by a north-westerly gale off the east of Scotland, even an extra six inches may make all the difference between safety and disaster.

The three factors which we have so far considered— relative position of sun and moon, winds and barometric pressure—affect the level of the water all along the coast. There is a fourth factor which is operative in river estuaries, and that is the state of the river itself. The floods which result from heavy rain are naturally worst above the reach of the tides, but they also help to raise the level in the lower reaches, and though this can only be a secondary factor, it happens that many of the floods which have caused damage and loss of life in London during the past century have occurred in very wet years. Thus 1852, the second wettest year of the nineteenth century, brought one of the highest Thames floods on record ; in this year the river was so swollen that, on the occasion of the Duke of Wellington's funeral, the hearse and horses were upset in the flooded Bath Road at Maidenhead, this being known as " The Duke of Wellington's Flood." At Putney the towing path was six feet under water, and the Great Western line was flooded for four miles between Hanwell and Paddington. In the relatively dry years between 1852 and the 'seventies there were no notable floods, but the long series of wet years that followed brought the great London floods of November 15th, 1875, and January 2nd, 1877.

There seems no doubt that the removal of old London Bridge in 1831 increased the liability of London to tidal floods. This historic bridge was constructed in 1209, and was an affair of great solidity. The piers were very broad, and the arches between them were so narrow that nothing larger than a wherry could pass. In the eighteenth century this became so inconvenient that the two centre arches were combined to allow barges to pass, but even so, the total space between the piers was considerably less than the space occupied by the solid masonry. The water used to pour through the arches in veritable cataracts, the difference between the level on one side of the bridge and that on the other sometimes amounting to several feet, and the force of the water was so great that it was employed to work the water-wheels by means of which London was supplied with water. The passage of the arches in a boat was like shooting a waterfall, and there were several fatal accidents. It is recorded that in 1429 the Duke of Norfolk was thrown into the water through his boat being capsized, and in 1628 Queen Henrietta nearly suffered the same mishap. The tides coming up the river expended a large part of their energy against this huge barrier, and above the bridge the rise and fall of the tides was appreciably smaller than at present, and less likely to cause serious flooding by itself, though of course it must be remembered that in those days London was not so well barricaded against the Thames as it is now. On the other hand, the bridge held up the flow of the river, and in times of heavy rain prevented its water from escaping readily, and this accentuated the danger of ordinary river floods. The immediate effect of the removal of the bridge was to lower the water-level of low tide to such an extent that navigation was interfered with, and it became necessary to dredge out the river bed—a process which incidentally resulted in the discovery of many interesting antiquities. The dredging was assisted by the increased scour of the tides, and soon formed a deep channel up which the tidal water could run freely. The average level of high tide at Battersea and neighbouring parts of London became more than a foot above that experienced before the removal of the old bridge. The tidal flood problem became acute, and it was probably accentuated still further by the rebuilding of Westminster Bridge in 1862 and Blackfriars Bridge in 1869, and was perhaps one of the reasons which led to the building of the Thames embankments in 1869 to 1874. The highest tide on record before the removal of the old bridges was that of December 7th, 1663, which submerged Whitehall; it has been calculated that this tide rose to $16\frac{1}{2}$ feet above the present Ordnance datum. This height must have been due to an exceptional combination of circumstances, for more than two hundred years were to elapse before it was exceeded. From 1874 to 1882, however, it was exceeded no fewer than six times, and although in the succeeding period of relatively dry years the tides remained within more moderate bounds, the general level of high tide has shown a steady increase during the present century, and the recent flood tide of January, 1928, overtopped all records. That this increase is due to conditions within the river and not to some change in the nature of the tides themselves is clearly shown by the fact that at Crossness and Woolwich there has been no appreciable change during the thirty years from 1898 to 1927, while at Chelsea the average level of high tides has risen by three inches, and at Hammersmith by six inches. Such a progressive increase as one passes up the river must be

mainly due to the decreased resistance to the flow of the
tide, brought about by a deepening of the channel.

It seems probable, however, that this gradual rise in the
level of the highest tides must be attributed in part to yet
another set of causes, including the growth of Greater
London, which resulted in the replacement of large areas
of porous soil by roofs and other impervious surfaces, the
improvement of drainage, and the construction of smooth
tarred road surfaces, off which water runs rapidly. One of
the main causes for this type of road-making was the dust
nuisance caused by motor vehicles, and it is a curious
example of cause and effect that the development of motor-
ing may have increased the liability of London to flooding.
It is possible that the conversion of a number of small open
streams into drains also had some effect. It does seem to
be true that a heavy downpour of rain affects the level of
the Thames more rapidly than formerly, and it is difficult
to assign any other adequate causes.

We can now come to the actual circumstances attending
the flood of January 7th, 1928, as described in the *Meteorological Magazine* for the following February.

We have seen in Chapter II that the year 1927 was abnormally wet. It is true that December on the whole was drier
than usual, but in winter evaporation is small, and these
few dry weeks did little to mitigate the sodden condition of
the ground. At Christmas came heavy rain, changing into
the memorable snowstorm which piled up a foot of snow
in southern England, and much more in drifts on the hills,
and dislocated road and rail transport to an extent unknown
since the great snowstorm of 1891. There was an abnormally
high tide on December 26th, but most of the snow stayed
on the ground until December 31st. At the end of the year
a thaw set in, and on January 2nd and 3rd the water represented by this accumulation of snow was pouring into the
rivers. The level of the Thames rose rapidly, and flooding
became widespread above London. The first week in January,
1928, was abnormally rainy in southern England, receiving
about twice its usual fall, and the country being water-

logged, all this rain was added to the thaw water of the snow. The floods above London became unusually extensive ; river-side dwellers are accustomed to mild floods almost every winter, but these extended beyond the usual flood limits, and some of the photographs taken at the time showed very striking conditions. The flow at Teddington weir, which is reckoned as 4,500 million gallons a day when the river is " bank high," was 5,200 million gallons on January 1st, and rose rapidly to 9,500 million gallons on the 7th, thus approaching the " record " flow of November, 1894. This proved to be the crest of the flood, however, for on that day the level of the upper reaches had already begun to fall.

While the crest of the river flood was nearing London, the other forces which control our river were rapidly shaping themselves for an effective climax. The time of new moon and spring tides was approaching, and the predicted height of high water at London Bridge on the early morning of the 7th, that is, the height which the water would attain if all the meteorological factors were normal, was 21 feet above Admiralty datum, or 12 feet 6 inches above Ordnance datum. This is not especially high, for on occasion the predicted height may reach 25 feet above Admiralty datum, but, combined with the swollen state of the river and the disturbed weather conditions, it proved to be too high for safety. The weather was very stormy. During the 6th a deep depression travelled rapidly across Scotland in an east-south-easterly direction, and in the rear of this depression the wind rose to a gale from north over the North Sea during the evening. Thus the conditions described above as most liable to cause tidal floods—gales from the right direction, spring tide and high river—were all present, and the water rose to a height of nearly six feet above the predicted height. London was not prepared for such an abnormal occurrence, and the river defences were overtopped or penetrated at a number of points in the City, Southwark, Westminster and westward to Putney and Hammersmith. A good deal of riverside London is below the level of spring tides, and a large amount of damage was inevitable, but the greater part of the death-roll of fourteen consisted of people who were sleeping in basements and were trapped by the water rushing down the stairs.

Very similar weather conditions to those of January 6th, 1928, occurred on November 1st, 1921, when northerly and north-westerly gales prevailed over the North Sea during the morning, moderating over eastern England by midday. The spring tide of the afternoon was predicted to reach the unusual height of 25 feet above Admiralty datum, and although the River Thames was unusually low in consequence of the long drought, this height was exceeded by about a foot. The water covered the tramlines on the Embankment, and wharves in the City were flooded. The importance of the wind is shown by the fact that the spring tide of September 24th, 1926, which was predicted to rise to the same height as that of November 1st, 1921, caused no flooding, because the winds were light. There was a serious flood on January 18th, 1881, which resulted from the coincidence of a spring tide with a gale from north-east in the North Sea, east in the Thames estuary and south-east in the Channel, and the break-up of a severe frost; the damage on this occasion was accentuated by the floating ice.

No account of the Thames floods would be complete without a reference to those of November, 1894, although, being due wholly to rain and not associated with any abnormal tides, they were not serious below Richmond and Twickenham. The rain which caused this flood was really exceptional. On the twenty-six days, October 23rd to November 17th, more than eight inches of rain fell in the Thames valley, or nearly one-third of the average annual fall. Eight inches of rain in the Thames valley is 1,950 million tons, or 440,000 million gallons of water, and if this quantity had flowed off in twenty-six days without any loss by evaporation or percolation, the flow of the Thames at Teddington would have been 17,000 million gallons a day. The evaporation in a wet November is very small, but a good deal of the rain managed to soak into the ground;

PLATE II—RIVER BANK, EAST MOLESEY, NOVEMBER 17TH, 1894

(By permission o the Royal Meteorological Society)

even so, the flow at Teddington at one time exceeded 11,000 million gallons a day. When the river is " bank high " the flow is reckoned as 4,500 million gallons, so that the amount of water pouring into Richmond was more than two and a half times the amount which the Thames can dispose of in comfort. The final blow came during the four days November 11th to 14th, when two very intense depressions passed along the Thames valley and delivered 3·22 inches of rain, or more than usually falls in the whole of November. It is small wonder that a large part of the area above London was flooded. It is remarkable how persistently the heavy rainfall was limited to the Thames valley throughout October and November, for the rest of the country escaped with little more than an average fall.

A few details of earlier tidal floods, both in the Thames and in other parts of the country, may be of interest. The earliest recorded Thames flood, in A.D. 9, which destroyed many inhabitants, may have been either tidal or riverine. In A.D. 60 a storm flood ravaged the coasts of Britain and Gaul, and in 80 there was a great flood in the Severn. In A.D. 245 many thousand acres in Lincolnshire were flooded by the sea and have never been recovered, while in 419 the coast of Hampshire was overwhelmed. Floods occurred in the Humber about A.D. 530 and at Glasgow in 738 ; of the latter it is recorded that more than 400 families were drowned.

The period from the eleventh to the fifteenth centuries was exceptionally stormy in the North Sea, and a series of great tidal floods struck like the blows of a battering-ram against the sea defences of Holland, until they broke through and submerged a large area of fertile ground, forming the Zuyder Zee. According to a theory put forward by O. Pettersson, the positions of the sun and moon were such as to cause a period of unusually great tidal range about 1434, which he associated with these disasters. The series began in 1086, which was followed by a much more serious disaster on November 11th, 1099, when a violent storm at high tide flooded the coasts of Holland and England as far south as

Kent, causing 100,000 deaths ; the Thames did not escape. In the following year it is recorded that " the Thames did rise with such high springs and tides that many towns were drowned." Other " storm-floods " occurred in 1134, 1135 and 1162, but the first intimation of the great calamity which was to befall Holland did not occur until 1218, when on November 17th an enormous storm-flood overwhelmed a number of parishes, and is stated to have drowned 100,000 people. Two months later there was a death-roll reported as 36,000, and other blows followed in February and September, 1221, January, 1222, and January, 1223. On October 1st, 1250, there was a very great storm-flood in the North Sea, which still further wrecked the Dutch sea defences and increased the area of the Zuyder Zee, converting Wieringen into an island. It also caused much damage in Kent, for in Winchelsea 300 houses and many churches were destroyed. After a smaller flood in 1277, Boston was struck by a great flood and gale in 1282, in which the monastery of Spalding and many churches were destroyed. " At Yarmouth, Donwich and Ipchurch an intolerable multitude of men, women and children were overwhelmed by the waters, especially at Bostone." Again, in November, 1334, a very great wind caused a sea-flood on the east coast. In this connection Mr. G. M. Meyer informs us that a passage in the works of Sir Thomas Browne records that in the time of Edward III (1327–77) the tides in the Humber rose four feet higher than they formerly did. On January 16th, 1362, another storm-flood drowned thirty parishes in Eastern Friesland and Schleswig, and gave the Friesian islands their present form. The final blow came on November 19th, 1421 ; a great flood broke over Friesland, Holland and England, in which seventy-two places were submerged and 100,000 people drowned. In this storm the Zuyder Zee finally reached its present form. The last storm of the series occurred on April 10th, 1446, a violent gale being associated with thunder, very heavy snow and terrible cold in Europe, while in the North Sea there was a fearful storm-flood which drowned sixteen places ; the loss of life is again estimated at 100,000.

This stormy period in the North Sea during the twelfth to the fourteenth centuries is of great interest. Man had not only to contend with tidal floods ; in addition, records of very wet years were unusually frequent and droughts were unusually rare, so that the rainfall of the whole period must have been exceptionally heavy. Moreover, the annalists often refer to the severity of the winters, pointing like the high tides to frequent northerly winds. The whole conjunction of circumstances very strongly suggests that for some reason deep barometric depressions made a habit of settling down over the southern part of the North Sea. This type of pressure distribution, while it brings heavy rainfall over the greater part of Britain, concentrates its worst efforts in the east, a state of affairs which recurred in the wet years of the 'seventies described in Chapter V.

On October 5th, 1571, according to Lowe, " a tremendous gale and flood occurred between Hammerston and Grimsby ; 20,000 cattle and sheep perished, houses were blown down, bridges washed away, and many ships wrecked. Bourne was overflowed to midway of the church's height ; boats road over St. Neot's church walls." Much damage was done all down the coast of Kent. On September 21st, 1555, the King's Palace at Westminster and Westminster Hall were flooded as a result of a spring tide, heaped up by the wind, meeting a river swollen by rains.

The flood of January 20th, 1607, was very disastrous in the Severn estuary. Stow records that " the waters rose above the tops of the houses," and the event is commemorated by a painted board in the church at Kingston Seymour, between Yatton, Clevedon and Weston-super-Mare, a copy of which has kindly been supplied by Mr. J. Harger Pye, Engineer of the Clevedon Gas and Water Company. In connection with the date it must be remembered that in those days the calendar year ended on March 31st instead of December 31st :

" Jan. 20th 1606 and 4 Jas. I an inundation of the Sea Water by overflowing and breaking down the Sea banks happd in the Parish of Kingstone-Seamore and many others

G

adjoining by reason whereof many persons were drowned and much Cattle and Goods were lost, the water in the Church was five feet high and the greater part lay on the Ground about 10 days." The floods extended along the coast for some twenty miles, and in some places the water reached a depth of twelve feet, and the flood, coming suddenly and unexpectedly about 9 o'clock in the morning, " the soone being most fayrely and brightly spred," caused much loss of life. Like the Thames flood of 1928, it was due to an unusually high spring tide encountering an unusual run-off in the River Severn, but in that estuary such conditions may result in the formation of a true " tidal wave." Other parts of the country suffered in the same storm, which must have been very violent and widespread, for in the Fen district very large areas were flooded, and at Broom Hill, in Romney Marsh, four miles from Rye, the sea came in so outrageously that one Master Bury lost 1,162 sheep, and it did not appear as if the area could ever be reclaimed from the sea.

The tidal flood of 1703 in the Thames Valley has already been referred to ; the violent south-west winds which accompanied the storm of November 27th of that year— probably the worst storm ever experienced in this country —also drove large quantities of water up the Bristol Channel, and flooded the shores, causing a great deal of damage. In 1791 there was so high a tide that " boats came through the passage of Old Palace Yard from the Thames and round up to Westminster Hall Gate." This brings us to the tidal floods of 1852 and the 1870's, to which reference has already been made.

Equally disastrous with tidal floods in the suddenness of their onset are the floods which rise in narrow mountain valleys as the result of heavy downpours of rain. Among our examples of these, the Moray floods of August, 1829, may fairly be described as unique in the British Islands, at least since instrumental rainfall observations began. The rainfall which caused the floods was of extraordinary intensity, great persistence, and fell over a wide area, and the total volume of water concerned in the floods was enormous. The amount of damage was very great, in spite of the comparative sparseness of the population in the flooded areas. The heaviest rain fell mainly in the upper parts of the valleys of the Rivers Nairn, Findhorn and Spey. Rain began to fall on the evening of the 2nd, and continued with little interruption until the morning of the 4th. The downpour came mainly with a north-east wind, and its force was such that it penetrated all doors and windows facing in that direction. At Huntley Bridge 3¾ inches fell during the twenty-four hours ending at 5 a.m. on the 4th, but this was some distance from the region of heaviest rain, where unfortunately no gauges were in operation. Large numbers of game were destroyed, and it is said that this was due not to hailstones or to large raindrops, but to the way in which the drops were crowded together, so that the rain seemed to fall almost like a mass of water. The Findhorn at its greatest height filled its valley, 200 yards wide, to a level 17 feet above the normal height of the water ; the level is marked by a tablet, and on a fine summer afternoon its record seems almost incredible. Practically all this rise must have resulted from the rainfall of the thirty-six hours ; the melting of snow on the mountains may have added a little, but the preceding months had been generally warm and dry. In fact the state of the ground before the rain must have diminished rather than exaggerated the flooding.

This flood was very quickly followed by another, on the 27th of the same month. The heavy rain which caused the second flood was more local, being confined mainly to the Nairn Valley and Inverness district, but in some parts it was even more intense, and many houses which survived the first flood were destroyed by the second. These two floods were undoubtedly more severe than any which have since occurred in that part of Scotland, though the visitations of 1849, 1868 and 1892 were all sufficiently noteworthy.

The storm of January 24th to 26th, 1849, is usually referred to as the " Inverness " flood because that town suffered most from the flooding which ensued. Loch Ness,

twenty-four miles long, rose about 14 feet, a height unequalled in its annals. About a third of the town to the west
of the River Ness was inundated to a depth of two or three
feet, and the famous old stone bridge, which then carried
most of the traffic across the river, was destroyed. The
heavy rain responsible for the flood fell mostly on the mountains, the storm area extending as far south as the Grampians,
and in spite of the winter season, it was accompanied by a
thunderstorm.

The floods of 1868 also caused a great deal of damage
in the Inverness district. Towards the end of January heavy
rain fell over the whole of Scotland and northern England,
but it was in the Highlands that the streams and rivers
rose most rapidly and the worst damage was done. On
January 30th Loch Ness rose twelve inches in seven hours.
Another alarming flood occurred on February 7th, but this
was only an echo of the first, resulting from the high level
of the river, in conjunction with a spring tide and a westerly
gale in the Atlantic.

In January, 1892, heavy snow fell in the Highlands between
the 5th and 9th, forming a deep covering, piled by a violent
wind into drifts unequalled for over thirty years, and many
trains were snowbound. This snow cover persisted until the
28th, but the thaw, when it came, was very rapid, and the
floods which resulted were greater than any since 1829. The
floods were most severe in the Strathglass, Bonar Bridge
and Strathspey areas. Bonar Bridge was destroyed, and parts
of the railway in Strathspey were washed away. This flood
was in fact remarkable for the number of bridges which
were destroyed, including several constructed by the
" Pontifex Maximus," the engineer Thomas Telford, who
designed the Menai Suspension Bridge.

After these four floods at intervals of about twenty years,
the Highlands of Scotland have suffered less severely. This
may be because the stone bridges destroyed in 1892 were
for the most part replaced by iron structures which are at
the same time stronger and less of a hindrance to the free
run-off of the water. Whether the depths of rain which

fell in these four storms have since been equalled we cannot tell for certain, since even now there are not always rain-gauges where the rain is heaviest. Reading of the amount of damage done, however, one feels that they cannot have fallen far short of, and may well have exceeded, the four great storms of East Anglia in 1912, Bruton in 1917, Louth in 1921, and Cannington in 1924.

That this is not an idle speculation is shown by the report published in the *Aberdeen Evening Gazette* of the damage caused by the heavy rains of October 1st to 4th, 1920, when over 7 inches was actually recorded in the mountains round Balmoral and Ballater : " It is doubtful whether at any time since ' the big spate of '29 ' the destruction has been so extensive as during the past few days. . . . Floods could scarcely have come at a more inopportune moment, and many thousands of sheaves of grain have been swept out to sea, as well as ricks of hay and straw. . . . Serious though the rainstorm has been, the great Moray floods of 1829 were more extensive as well as more disastrous. They are still the high-water mark of Scottish deluges."

The most remarkable storm on record in the neighbour-hood of Carrbridge occurred on July 8th, 1923. According to *The Times* of July 10th, " nearly 600 yards of permanent way on high embankments disappeared into the torrent of water, and a stretch of two miles, between Aviemore and Inverness, has been so much damaged that traffic cannot be resumed for at least a month." Floods had occurred in the same locality as recently as June, 1914, when special measures were taken to guard against subsequent rushes of flood water.

One of the worst floods in the Severn Valley occurred in May, 1886, and was caused mainly by the widespread and persistent cyclonic rains of May 11th to 13th. The total for these three days exceeded 5 inches over a large area, and reached 7·09 inches at Burwarton, near Brown Clee House, in Shropshire. At a station near Ludlow the rain-gauge, although it was twelve feet above the usual level of the river, was completely submerged by the flood. The high-water mark of this flood at Diglis Lock, just below Worcester, is still preserved ; it is only a few inches below that of 1770, which is the highest on record, and it has not since been equalled.

Thunderstorms and " cloud-bursts " have caused many sudden and destructive floods in hilly districts. Some examples from recent years which provided " record " rainfalls are described in Chapter XIII, but there have been other floods as great or greater for which no measurement of the rainfall are available. The most intense rains are usually very local, and often there is no rain-gauge in the immediate neighbourhood, while on other occasions the rain-gauge has been flooded or washed away. Occasionally it is possible to form an idea of the amount of rainfall from the height reached by streams running off a small catchment area. At Todmorden, in the south-west of Yorkshire, a deluge of rain fell on July 9th, 1870, and a stream 4 feet 6 inches deep ran down a road 34 feet wide for two hours. The depth of rain over the gathering ground was estimated as about 9 inches, and this storm would rank as one of the heaviest falls in a day.

A visitation of this nature, described as a " thunderstorm and cloud-burst," occurred near Driffield on July 3rd, 1892. The rain was so intense that the water came down from the higher ground in a sheet about 100 yards wide and 3 feet deep, running at twenty to thirty miles an hour, with a sound like the roaring of the sea. It is said that a threshing-machine weighing five tons was carried forty feet. A similar storm occurred on Rombald's Moor, between Bingley and Ilkley, in the early afternoon of July 12th, 1900, which washed boulders weighing several tons each down into the road. At Ilkley, where the damage was much less, 5·40 inches of rain was recorded, and on the moor the amount may well have reached 9 inches.

During the afternoon of August 3rd, 1883, a violent storm, described as " a waterspout of unprecedented magnitude," burst on the Ochil Hills between Dollar and Alva. The flood came so suddenly that people who had crossed the

main street at Alva only three minutes before had almost
to swim back to their homes. From a baker's shop five
bags of flour and casks of butter floated a distance of
100 yards. Alva is built on a terrace above the low ground
at the foot of the hills, and directly opposite a deep, narrow
valley. It was no doubt the water coming down the valley
which caused the sudden flood.

A violent thunderstorm in South Wales on September 4th,
1886, presented some curious features. At Dowlais there
was a particularly intense thunderstorm during the afternoon, but without much wind. This was suddenly followed
by a " violent whirlwind," which lasted only a few seconds
but blew in windows in many parts of the town, and knocked
over men and even a pony. At Swansea the damage was
more serious. During the afternoon a " waterspout " was
seen to travel from the bay towards Kelvey Hill. The latter
is about 650 feet high, and the upper part is almost vertical,
while on the lower slopes some rows of houses had been
built. When the waterspout struck the hill great torrents
of water rushed down the slopes, burst through the upper
row of houses, and carried all the movable contents into
the street below. Many people were washed from a back
room into a front room, out of the door and down the hill.
It was estimated that 8,000 tons of earth and rock were
carried down by these torrents, while forty families were
rendered homeless. On the day of this storm none of the
rainfall stations round Swansea recorded as much as two
inches, and this raises the question whether the torrents of
water which fell on Kelvey Hill were really rain. The violent
whirlwinds known as tornadoes are sometimes capable of
lifting fairly heavy objects into the air, and these must fall
somewhere. Most of the phenomena described as " water-
spouts " are probably only revolving masses of cloud, but
when a tornado passes over the sea or a pond a good deal
of water may be drawn into it. It is recorded that two
" pipe-like " objects were seen near Banbury in November,
1873, and when one of these passed over a pool nearly all
the water was drawn up at least 60 feet and carried

horizontally about 200 yards before it was dropped. If it had happened to fall on a rain-gauge we might have had an " unprecedented " rainfall. Not only the water, but the other contents of the ponds, are drawn up, and thus we have authentic records of showers of small frogs, fish or snails. Of a similar nature, but originating on land instead of in water, are showers of hay, corn and hazel-nuts.

This lifting action has been actually experienced in a waterspout. The clipper ship, *Crest of the Wave*, near the Greek Archipelago on August 20th, 1855, passed right through a waterspout, which zigzagged across the deck. A witness wrote : " For a few moments my sensation was that of being drawn aloft with the spiral motion of the spray and water, not in the least of being crushed to the deck by a heavy volume of water." All the crew escaped with nothing worse than a bath.

Disastrous floods have sometimes been caused by the collapsing of the embankments of reservoirs, suddenly releasing large volumes of water. Among the more recent disasters of this character were those at Dolgarrog, in North Wales, and Skelmorlie, near Greenock. Above Dolgarrog the water is stored in an artificial reservoir formed by an embankment three-quarters of a mile long and 25 feet above the ordinary lake level, and in its passage through pipes to the River Conway below, the water drives turbines which convert its energy into electric power, utilised to produce high temperatures whereby the natural clays of the locality are converted to pure aluminium. In November, 1925, following heavy rains in Snowdonia, this embankment gave way, and great damage occurred in the outskirts of the bungalow town which had sprung up as a result of this new industry.

During the wet year 1852, celebrated for the " Duke of Wellington's Flood " in the Thames (see p. 90), there were also extensive floods in the north of England, as a result of which the Bilberry dam, near Huddersfield, burst on February 4th. The village of Holmforth was almost destroyed, with great loss of life.

Very serious damage followed the failure of the earth

embankment of the Bradfield Reservoir on March 11th, 1864, when 245 lives were lost. With practically no warning the water burst through a gap 100 yards wide at the top and 70 feet deep, and 40,000 cubic feet of water rushed down the valley at the rate of about eighteen miles an hour. The reservoir was eight miles to the west of Sheffield, and there was much damage in that city. Between Rotherham and Doncaster there was an extraordinary rise in the river, but the inundation did not excite serious alarm. In all some 4,357 houses were flooded, 798 being destroyed and abandoned. Over £2,300 was spent in carting away mud and cleansing the district, while it is reported that £370,000 was paid out in compensation.

PART II

DROUGHTS

CHAPTER VIII

THE CAUSES OF DROUGHT

" This subject, as I understand it, is not very well understood."
Schoolboy's Essay

IN Chapter I we discussed the various influences at work
on the pressure distribution over the eastern North Atlantic,
which bring about a period of wet, stormy and unsettled
weather over the British Isles. We found that such a wet
season may belong to one of two types, which were distinguished as *cyclonic* and *orographic*. In the cyclonic type
the Icelandic low is shifted a considerable distance to the
southward, so that pressure is lowest over the British Isles
and a succession of barometric depressions passes across
Ireland and England, or along the English Channel, giving
relatively heavy rainfall over the southern half of the country.
In the orographic type, on the other hand, the Icelandic
low becomes more intense than usual, and this, combined
perhaps with a small shift to the southward or south-eastward,
causes exceptionally strong south-west winds, which bring
heavy rainfall on our western highlands.

The distributions of pressure associated with long droughts
in this country are in the main the reverse of those associated
with long rainy spells, but there are some important modifi-
cations. By far the most frequent cause of a long period of
settled fine weather in England is a north-easterly extension
of the Azores anticyclone towards or over the British Isles.
At the same time the Icelandic low retreats far to the north-
east, towards the Arctic Ocean ; the main tracks of depressions run well to the north, and only the north-west of
Scotland comes to any extent under their influence. The
average distribution of pressure during the intense and

prolonged drought of 1921 is shown in Fig. 8. It will be seen
that a ridge of high pressure from the Azores anticyclone
extended over the south-west of Ireland, on the north of
which the isobars are fairly close together. Hence the winds
on the west coast were fairly strong, and brought a moderate
amount of orographic rainfall to the western hills of Ireland
and Scotland. To the east and north-east of this high pressure
ridge, however, conditions were different. The isobars spread

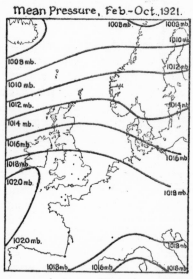

FIG. 8—MEAN PRESSURE, FEBRUARY–OCTOBER, 1921

out fanwise, and this means that the air which crossed a
comparatively narrow stretch of Irish coast must also have
spread out over almost the whole of England. For example,
the air which crossed the southern half of the west coast of
Ireland between Galway and Valentia actually fanned out so
much that over southern and eastern England it extended
from the Scilly Isles to the north of Yorkshire. Such a
broadening of the air current not only means that the general
wind velocity must become very light, but also that a good
deal of air must be brought down from above to help fill

up the gap. Descending air is automatically warmed and dried by compression, and in a region where the isobars spread out fanwise in this manner the weather must be fine. It was just this region of fanning out which suffered most during the drought of 1921.

During this drought a curious phenomenon occurred on several occasions, which attracted the notice of the Press and which may perhaps be attributed to the descent of the air. With a westerly wind, a mass of heavy clouds would drift overhead, the air would become colder, and there would be every sign that a heavy shower was about to fall. There might even be a few drops of rain, but then the clouds would break up and pass away without relieving the parched ground. The generally high temperature must also have contributed to this result, since air coming in from the Atlantic absorbed heat all the time during its passage across England, and therefore became relatively drier. In any ordinary year this absorption of heat by the lower layers of air would generally end in a thunderstorm, but in 1921 it seems merely to have contributed towards the general dryness.

The distribution shown in Fig. 8 represents the average conditions over a period of nine months. During a good deal of this time there was a closed anticyclone or area of high pressure directly over the British Isles—a sort of offshoot which had become detached from the Azores anticyclone. This in summer gives us our very finest weather, with cloudless skies day after day, but in most years it rarely lasts beyond a week or ten days. In 1921, however, such anticyclones sometimes persisted for week after week.

It will be readily seen that this type of pressure distribution leads to a distribution of rainfall which is the direct antithesis of the cyclonic type. Where cyclonic rainfall is heaviest, at least relatively to the average rainfall, anticyclonic drought is most intense, while the rainfall in the Western Highlands of Scotland is hardly affected. Since this type of drought is by far the more frequent, the immunity of northwest Scotland is one of the factors which give the rainfall of that region its remarkable regularity from year to year. Of the nine chief droughts of the past seventy years, on fewer than seven, namely, those of 1864, 1868, 1880, 1887, 1893, 1896 and 1921, were of this anticyclonic type.

The second type of drought occurred in 1895 and 1911. It is nearly, but not quite, the antithesis of the orographic type of rainy season. Its characteristic is that pressure is higher than usual to the north of the British Isles and lower than usual to the south, so that the normal fall of pressure from south to north is greatly weakened or even reversed. The orographic type of rainy season is associated with un-usually low pressure to the north-west, in the direction of Iceland, but in this type of drought the pressure is relatively highest rather to the north-east, over Scandinavia, than towards Iceland. If the differences from the average pressure are large, as in February and March, 1895, pressure is actually higher to the north than to the south of this country, and in place of the usual south-west winds we have a period of easterly winds. Over the British Isles pressure is generally a little above normal, and the majority of depressions pass well to the south, across the Bay of Biscay or northern Spain.

This type of drought is generally felt over the whole country. In February to June, 1895, the actual deficit of rainfall was greatest in the Western Highlands of Scotland, which suffered from the cutting off of the supply of orographical rain, but expressed as a proportion of the average rainfall, the loss was equally great in south-eastern and central England, where the east winds had little opportunity to pick up moisture during their passage across the North Sea. Both in the Western Highlands and the Thames valley the rainfall was less than half the average during these five months. During this drought only one region received more than its average amount, a small area on the north-east coast of Scotland, to which the east winds brought orographic rainfall from the North Sea. The drought of 1911 was partly of the anti-cyclonic, partly of the east wind type, and the distribution of rainfall was irregular. The driest region was in north-east Scotland, and four areas received slightly more than their normal amount—the extreme north-west of Scotland, Carnarvonshire, the south-eastern corner of Ireland, and, lastly, Gloucestershire and Worcestershire.

The reversal of the normal pressure distribution characteristic of an east wind drought is not usually stable, being, so to speak, a local unnatural revolt against a world-wide tendency for the highest pressure to occur in subtropical latitudes. Hence this second type of drought is not usually either prolonged or intense. It can, however, be very aggravating while it lasts. The air, owing to its origin over the continent of Europe, is dry and dusty, and can be very cold in winter and very hot in summer. February, 1895, when this type was very highly developed, was one of the coldest months ever experienced in England, with almost continuous skating. On the other hand, August, 1911, was one of the hottest months on record, and the shade temperature of 100° F. at Greenwich on August 10th is the highest officially accepted temperature since records began. The lack of rain is accentuated by the " burning " quality of the air, which is far more destructive to vegetation than the more genial, because somewhat moister, heat of the anticyclonic droughts in summer. Perhaps the worst example of an east wind drought in this country was that of 1252, described in Chapter XII. This forcibly recalls the words of Hosea, which, though of course they refer to quite a different climate, may be quoted here :

" Though he be fruitful among his brethren
An east wind shall come,
The breath of the Lord coming up from the wilderness,
And his spring shall become dry,
And his fountain shall be dried up ;
He shall spoil the treasure of all pleasant vessels."

These pressure distributions, however, are only the immediate causes or associates of drought. When we go back to more remote causes, we are in the same difficulty as in Chapter I, the possible causes are so many, and their complexity is so great, that no single cause suffices, and we have to look for the combination of a variety of factors. In one

H

respect, however, the problem of droughts is somewhat simpler than that of wet seasons. The latter are fairly evenly divided between the orographic and the cyclonic types, which require different types of pressure distribution ; on the other hand, the great majority of droughts are of the anticyclonic type. The essential condition for the development of the latter appears to be an area of low pressure over the Arctic Ocean. Low or high pressure in the Arctic is much more persistent than over Western Europe. In the British Isles the fact that pressure is below normal in one month does not make it any more probable that pressure will be below normal in the following month. At Spitsbergen, on the other hand, if pressure is below normal in one month there is a distinct likelihood that it will remain below normal during the following month. An examination of the severe anticyclonic droughts from 1864 to 1921 shows that, with one doubtful exception in 1879–80, the average pressure over the Arctic regions was lower than usual during the six months preceding the oncoming of dry weather in Britain. Hence it seems that one of the causes of droughts must be sought in the Arctic regions.

In discussing the causes of rainy seasons, we found that the general circulation of the atmosphere was of some importance, but that it was rather overridden by more local factors, such as the Gulf Stream, the Labrador Current, and ice off East Greenland or Iceland. In dealing with droughts it seems as if the reverse might happen, and the general or world-wide conditions be more important than the local ones. This is not to say that local effects are without importance, but it is curious that they are far less obvious than in the periods immediately preceding rainy seasons. Thus, in the seven droughts from 1868 onwards, the north-east trade wind was stronger than usual on four occasions, weaker than usual on two and normal on one. From 1893 onwards, two droughts were preceded by stronger, and three by weaker south-east trades. Not one of the droughts was preceded by remarkably abnormal conditions in either trade-wind. With the Labrador Current the story is the same ; in some cases it was stronger than usual, in others weaker, but only once were the conditions really unusual. In the winter of 1894 to 1895, this ice-bearing current was unusually weak—a strange forerunner of one of the coldest Februarys on record. Similarly with the ice-conditions, in the Greenland Sea the ice conditions preceding or accompanying drought have been four times weak, three times severe, and once normal. Off Iceland there has been little ice on four occasions, much ice on five, but nothing really exceptional. It is evident that there is nothing to help us here.

Since we are unable to call in local conditions to explain droughts, it seems that we must fall back on the more general, perhaps world-wide, fluctuations which are related to the general circulation of the atmosphere. One arm of that circulation is formed by the westerly winds in temperate latitudes. Near the surface in the northern hemisphere these winds are interrupted by the great continents of North America and Eurasia, but they are much more continuous at the level of the clouds. The higher clouds especially, almost always move from west to east. We can compare this continuous eastward movement to that of water vigorously stirred in a glass in such a way that it runs round and round in the same direction. Everyone knows what happens —the water collects near the sides of the glass and leaves a hole or dimple in the middle. In the same way the air in the upper layers of the atmosphere circulating round and round the pole, tends to collect in middle latitudes and leave a region of low pressure near the poles. It is owing to local accidents that at sea level the lowest pressure is found near Iceland and the Aleutian Islands ; at high levels the lowest pressure is probably farther north. Hence, any increase in the strength of the westerly winds should mean that air is withdrawn from the levels above the Arctic Ocean, and since it has to go somewhere, it generally elects to go to the latitude of Ireland and England—about 50–55° N. Why it should favour these latitudes in particular is something of a mystery, but it happens that the distance between the North Pole and Central England, 35° of latitude, is just about the same as the distance between the Icelandic low and the centre of the Azores anticyclone under normal conditions, and it may be that 35° is the distance apart which neighbouring areas of high and low pressure like to maintain.

As to what causes the speeding-up of the west winds, we are somewhat at a loss. Theoretically, it should be an increase in the difference of temperature between equatorial and polar regions, and no doubt that is one of the ultimate causes, but there are many complications. There seems to be a sort of slow surge of air from one part of the world to another, for example, between America and the Old World, which originates in the Argentine or even farther south over the Antarctic, and it is quite possible that it is to unknown changes at the opposite ends of the earth that we shall have to look for the causes of our great anticyclonic droughts. This may be another illustration of the truth that meteorology cannot be treated on a parochial or even on a continental basis ; the world is one complex whole, and the climatic variations of its different parts are inter-related according to some plan which we are only now dimly beginning to guess.

Thus we see that there are probably certain world conditions which lead to a distribution of barometric pressure— relatively low over the Arctic Ocean, relatively high over middle latitudes—favourable to drought in the British Isles. Since pressure is normally lower over the Arctic than over Britain, this represents an accentuation of one feature of the normal distribution of pressure. This feature then becomes strong enough to dominate our weather conditions, and to reduce local factors, such as the Gulf Stream and Iceland ice, to the position of mere trifles. The reverse of the drought conditions, however—pressure relatively high over the Arctic Ocean and relatively low over Britain—tends to eliminate this feature of our normal pressure distribution, but without greatly affecting the Icelandic low. The latter then becomes the most important control of our weather, and, what is of even greater moment, it is, so to speak, set free from the chains which bind it to the neighbourhood of Iceland or the ocean to the north or north-east of that island. It becomes free to wander, and where it makes its home depends on just those local factors which we considered in Chapter I. We may compare our weather to our health ; when we are " fit " we have no ailments, but when our general health becomes poor, the precise nature of the illness which overtakes us—influenza, dyspepsia, blood poisoning or a nervous breakdown—is almost a matter of accident, and if we are fortunate, we may escape without serious trouble at all.

CHAPTER IX

THE DROUGHT OF 1921

" This is the driest thing I know."
" Alice in Wonderland "

WHEN the year 1921 opened with a wet January, no one had the slightest idea that we were at the beginning of one of the driest years on record in the British Isles. Even the small amount of knowledge which we now possess concerning the causes of wet and dry spells was then undiscovered, and everyone was resigned to the recurrence of another spring and summer of the rather damp and dismal character of the three preceding years. It was only as the months passed that one gradually came to realise that something exceptional was happening and that we were experiencing a season about which, in years to come, we might boast to our grandchildren as an example of what England could do in " the good old days."

One of the striking features of the drought of 1921 was its splendid isolation. The dry year 1887 began a run of years of which most were dry, just as the wet year 1872 occurred at the commencement of a definite run of wet years. The year 1921 resembled 1903 in that it occurred in a run of years of unlike rainfall. Reference has already been made to the apparent paradox that during the wet year 1903 there was some difficulty with water supply owing to the preceding run of dry years, which set in again in 1904. Similarly, 1921 was preceded and followed by a series of wet years. As early as 1914 Dr. H. R. Mill drew attention, in the annual reports to the Metropolitan Water Board, to the sequence of wet years in the Thames Valley, and pointed out that in any schemes for the supply of London with drinking water no reliance could be placed on the rainfall maintaining the level of the preceding years. The run of wet years was, however, so persistent in the south that from 1909 to 1927 the rainfall over the whole Thames Valley exceeded the average in as many as fifteen of the nineteen years.

The drought of 1921 can, however, be regarded as extending back to the fairly dry August of the preceding year. The rainfall of September, 1920, was about the average amount, but that of October, November and December showed considerable deficiencies in each month. January, 1921, was distinctly wetter than the average, but the excess only wiped off about half the accumulated deficiencies of the preceding five months. With the commencement of February the drought proper may be said to have set in. Less than the average for the month occurred everywhere. The whole of Wales, most of England and large areas in the East Midlands of Scotland and Ireland had less than a quarter of their average, while considerable areas in the north and south-west of England and Wales received less than 10 per cent. In fact, over the whole of England and Wales, the south-eastern half of Scotland and Central Ireland totals reaching one inch were rare. February, 1921, was not quite as dry as the same month in either 1895 or 1891, but with these exceptions it was the driest February on record in the last sixty years. There was a temporary break in the dry weather in March, when rather more than the average fell over the country generally. The subsequent months of 1921 were all markedly dry except August, when again the rainfall was just in excess of the average.

June was the most remarkable month of the whole year, being slightly drier over the country as a whole than even February, 1921. In this month the pressure was extremely high, and the usual Azores high pressure belt extended as far north as the western part of the British Isles. Over most of England, Wales, Ireland and the southern half of Scotland, the total rainfall for the month was less than one inch, while in certain small areas there was no rain during the whole month. Such an unusually dry spell occurred in parts of Kent, Sussex, Hampshire, the south-west of Wales and extreme south of Ireland. A whole calendar month free from rain is rare, and so far as information is available, only occurred in well-defined areas in February, 1891, April, 1893, July, 1911, April, 1912, June, 1921, and June, 1925. In each case the areas free from rain were in the southern half of the British Isles. Over the British Isles as a whole June, 1921, was the driest June since comparable statistics became available in 1870, but the subsequent June of 1925 was somewhat drier. The general values for the whole British Isles for the three driest Junes on record are set out below :

	Per cent. of Average	Inch
June, 1887 - - -	32	0·8
June, 1921 - - -	27	0·7
June, 1925 - - -	21	0·6

Although June, 1921, was not the driest month of any name on record for the British Isles as a whole, so far as can be ascertained only February, 1891, and June, 1925, were drier, while May, 1896, was about equally dry.

The three driest consecutive months of 1921 were April to June, when the rainfall over the British Isles generally was 58 per cent. of the average rainfall. The three months, November, 1879, to January, 1880, and May to July, 1868, were both more remarkable, but the effects of the summer shortage of 1921 were naturally more severe. The comments on record for July, 1868, stand out in striking contrast with those appropriate to the summers of recent years. " Another month of almost uninterrupted sunshine, which so baked the crust of the earth as seriously to injure much agricultural produce. . . . Sun-stroke was very frequent. Scarcely any rain fell, except at places where there were thunderstorms, and altogether the month can only be adequately described by one word—scorching. . . . Towards the end of the

month several towns in Lancashire were placed on short
water supply."

In the driest four months of 1921, April to July, the
fall over the British Isles was 63 per cent. of the average
amount in those months. The four months October, 1879,
to January, 1880, with 44 per cent., and March to June,
1893, with 52 per cent., were thus both much more remarkable. Some details of the dry winter of 1879 to 1880 which
followed the wet summer of 1879 have already been given
in Chapter V. The four months October, 1879, to January,
1880, were the driest of that winter, each receiving less than
half their respective average falls. This is the only instance
of so long a run of very dry months in the sixty years of
comparable statistics. The spring drought of 1893 was
equally memorable. While it lasted it was much more severe
than that of any other year, but it was relatively of short
duration. As many as twenty stations in the south-east of
England, mainly between London and the south-east coast,
recorded no rain on more than fifty consecutive days ; at
some of these there was a two months' drought from
March 17th to May 16th. Two stations in London recorded
no rain for seventy-two days, from March 4th to May 14th—
one of the longest runs of dry weather on record for these
islands. Another way of expressing the intensity of this
drought is that over most of the country to the south-east
of a line from London to Lyme Regis there were 100 days,
or more than three months, with less than an inch of rain.

The drought of 1921 included no long period of little
rain comparable with that of 1893. Moreover, we have seen
that there have been more remarkable periods of three and
four consecutive dry months. As longer series of months
are considered, the outstanding feature of 1921 becomes
apparent, its only rival for five or more consecutive dry
months being 1887. In each case 1887 was the drier over
the British Isles as a whole. If attention is confined to
England and Wales, then it can be claimed that 1921 is
without precedent for a run of five or more consecutive
dry months. The principal difference in the rainfall of the

two years was that in 1887 the severe drought was much
more widespread than in 1921, while in the latter year
certain areas, notably in the south-east of England, suffered
far more severely than in 1887. The rainfall of the six
months, February to July, over England and Wales was

FIG. 9—RAINFALL (INCHES), FEBRUARY–JULY, 1921

perhaps the most remarkable of this very dry year. As little
as half the usual amount fell during this period, which is
most unusual for so long a time and over so large an area.

A map showing the actual rainfall over England and
Wales during this period is shown as Fig. 9. The fall was

less than 5 inches over most of the south-east of England between the Isle of Wight and the Wash, and from the east of Kent to Birmingham and Ross. As small a fall also occurred over the Cheshire plain, in the neighbourhood of Doncaster and near Whitby. In three areas centred round Peterborough, Windsor and Colchester, there was less than 4 inches in the whole of the six months. The occurrence of little more than 10 inches in many parts of the usually wet areas of Dartmoor, Exmoor, Wales, the Lake District and the Pennines was nearly as remarkable. The map is in striking contrast with Fig. 4, which shows the rainfall of April to September, 1924, a wet period of similar length. Here the rainfall everywhere exceeded 12 inches, with as much as 70 inches in Snowdonia and the Lake District.

The difference between the distribution of rainfall in the two years 1921 and 1887 is shown by the general values set out below for the different parts of the British Isles, expressed as percentages of normal :

	1887	1921
	Per cent.	Per cent.
England and Wales -	74	70
Scotland - - -	80	99
Ireland - - -	77	88
British Isles - -	77	82

The rainfall of 1921 over the British Isles as a whole ranks as second smallest, while for England and Wales alone 1921 is the driest year. It is possible, so far as England alone is concerned, to compare the fall of 1921 with that during the last two centuries. There is no doubt that 1921 was the driest year since 1788, but beyond that it is only possible to say that the year 1921 was about as dry as any year since 1727, over England generally, but that the four years 1731, 1741, 1743 and 1788 were probably about equally dry.

In spite of the outstanding dryness of 1921 over England

as a whole, the year was the driest during the last sixty
years at individual stations representative of only two-thirds
of England, including most parts of southern England to
the south of a line passing through Liverpool, Rugby and

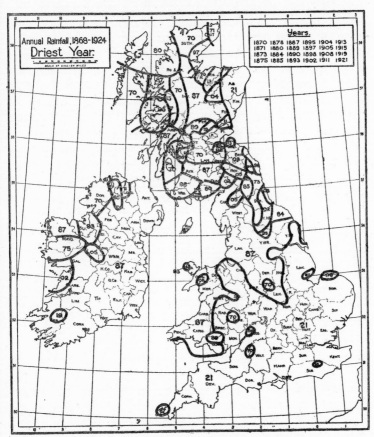

FIG 10.—ANNUAL RAINFALL, 1868–1924.   DRIEST YEAR

Hull (*see* Fig. 10). In the north, 1887 was the driest
year in most places. Records covering from 80 to 110 years
are available for Cirencester, Guernsey, Chichester, Spalding,
Oxford and Greenwich. In each case 1921 was by far the
driest year. In records for London back to 1774 there is

no indication of any comparable year. As London was by no means the driest district relative to the average, it may be justifiably inferred that in 1921 a considerable part of the south-east of England had the least rainfall for at least a century and a half, and probably for a still longer period, though complete statistical proof is wanting.

So much has been written about the dryness of 1921 that it is surprising to recall that certain parts of the British Isles recorded more than the usual amount of rain during this year. There was a small excess in Queen's County, but this was undoubtedly caused solely by the thunderstorm of June 26th, an isolated event in the course of the great summer drought. The areas with an excess in Great Britain were much more extensive and included the English Lake District and the whole of the western half of Scotland. This harmony between the Lake District and the Western Highlands is of common occurrence, and is undoubtedly associated with the similar mountainous character whereby both areas are subject to similar excesses or deficiencies of orographical rains. The contrast between the west and east of Scotland was much more remarkable. While Aberdeen received only 59 per cent. of the average annual rainfall, Inveraray Castle in the Highlands recorded 131 per cent. of the average there. The contrast in actual inches is even more striking. While at Aberdeen there was less than 19 inches during the year, at Loan at the head of Glenquoich, in Inverness-shire, a total of more than 200 inches was recorded. The explanation of this apparent anomaly is readily seen if we consider the distribution of pressure over north-western Europe. During the year as a whole, the average pressure over England and Wales and Ireland was high, nearly 5 mb. above the normal pressure. In the Faröe Islands, however, the pressure was practically normal, and still farther to the north-west, over Iceland, pressure was lower than usual. It will be recalled that, as shown in Fig. 1, pressure is generally lower over Iceland than over the British Isles, and it is this difference which causes our prevailing south-west winds. A decrease of pressure over Iceland, and an increase over the British Isles, accentuate the customary gradient of pressure, and thus lead to stronger and more persistent south-west winds on our north-western coasts. At the same time as an anticyclonic drought prevails over England and eastern Scotland, there is an increase in the amount of orographic rainfall over the Western Highlands.

While in Scotland the area with less than 60 per cent. of the average was small, in England the area so affected included most of the country south-east of a line drawn from Yarmouth to Plymouth. The contrast between Kent and Inverness is of particular interest. It has been shown that on the whole there is no connection between the simultaneous fluctuations in the rainfall of the south-east of England and that in the north-west. In some years, like 1921, the fluctuations at the two places are in direct opposition, while in others they are in agreement. Thus 1872, 1877 and 1903 were markedly wet in both districts. Indeed, it is broadly true to say that in some years the south of England and north of Scotland occupy two climatic zones with distinctive characteristics, while in other years the whole of the country belongs to one climatic zone.

The most astounding feature of 1921 was the deficiency in the rainfall in the south-east of England. The least rainfall likely to occur at any station in any one year had been regarded previously as 60 per cent. of the average. Records of this amount were extremely rare and, in the sixty years of detailed observations, occurred outside 1921 only in the one year 1887 and then only over a small area. In 1921 the area with less than 60 per cent. was not only large, but as little as 50 per cent. of the average was recorded over a well-defined part of east Kent. The rainfall in this region is quite unprecedented. The total of 10 inches recorded at Margate is by far the smallest on record for any part of the British Isles. The total number of days with rain was just short of 100, or 50 less than usual, and equally noteworthy. The monthly rainfall in this region deserves special comment. In the table below the rainfall of the series of driest consecutive months is set out for the Isle of Thanet.

RAINFALL OF THE DRIEST CONSECUTIVE MONTHS OF 1921
IN THE ISLE OF THANET

Months	Rainfall	
	Inches	Per cent. of Annual Average
1. July - - - -	·1	·5
2. June–July - -	·3	1·5
3. May–July - - -	1·2	5
4. April–July - - -	2·3	10
5. May–September - -	3·1	13
6. May–October - -	3·8	16
7. April–October - -	5·0	21
8. March–October - -	6·0	25
9. February–October -	6·7	28
10. February–November -	8·4	35
11. February–December -	9·7	41
12. January–December -	11·2	47

The rainfall of the periods of four or less consecutive
months, although small, is by no means unprecedented. The
actual rainfall, and the percentage of the annual average fall
for longer periods, are unprecedented in any other year, and
unequalled over any other part of the British Isles during
1921. In the most extreme conditions, therefore, rather
less than half the average rainfall has fallen in the driest
twelve consecutive months. In wet seasons in most parts
of the British Isles half the average annual rainfall has
fallen in only three consecutive months, while at a few
stations this amount has fallen in only two months.

So far as can be ascertained from the records of self-
recording instruments, the intensity of the rain during 1921
differed little from the normal. The feature of the rain of
1921 was its infrequency, such rain as did fall being of
normal intensity. One surprising feature, however, was the
unusually large number of heavy falls in twenty-four hours.
From 1911 to 1927 the average number of days during a
year on which a fall of 2·5 inches or more is recorded somewhere in the British Isles, has been 35 ; 1921 had 55 such

days, this being 9 more than any other year in the series and
20 more than the average. Similarly there were in 1921
35 days with falls exceeding 3 inches, compared with an
average of 19, second place being shared by 1920 and 1927
with 23 days.

The drought of 1921 extended over an unusually large slice
of the northern hemisphere. The rainfall for the year as a percentage of normal is shown in Fig. 11, in which the areas with
rainfall above normal are shaded, and those with rainfall
below normal are left unshaded, two areas which received
less than half their average amount being stippled. The
broken lines include areas with less than three-quarters of
their average fall. It will be seen that while the greater part of

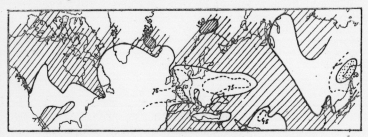

FIG. 11—RAINFALL OF 1921 AS PER CENT. OF AVERAGE
SHADED AREA, ABOVE AVERAGE ; STIPPLED AREA, VERY DRY

the United States had less than its usual fall, western Europe
and north-eastern Asia were the chief sufferers. The whole
of France, Belgium and Holland, and also a large part of
southern Russia and the central European countries, received
less than three-quarters of their average, while a large area
in France, and parts of Belgium and Italy, had less than
half, this especially dry area adjoining that in East Kent.
There was another large area with a deficiency of rain in
north-eastern Asia, where the coast of the Sea of Okhotsk
received little more than one-third of its usual total.

The dry area in western Europe suffered severely from
the shortage of water. In Belgium the drought from August,
1920, to October, 1921, was without precedent in historic
times, and during the most intense period from May to

I

October many stations recorded only one quarter or one-third of their usual rainfalls for these six months. It was necessary to close many factories and to limit the supply of water for domestic purposes, while the Lac de la Gileppe, which usually contains 460 million cubic feet of water, shrank so much that by the beginning of December it held barely 30 million cubic feet.

In France both the winter and spring of 1921 were un-usually dry. The drought attained a remarkable degree of severity in the summer, the months of June and August being especially dry and hot. In July forest and heath fires were very numerous in France, as well as in Belgium, Den-mark and Norway, but in southern France the drought was broken to some extent by a series of violent thunderstorms. Many mills and farmhouses were burnt down. At Beauvais, north of Paris, three crops of hay were cut during the year for the only time within living memory.

The drought was less severe in Germany than in either France or Russia, chiefly owing to a moderately wet and cool spring and early summer, and to some heavy thunder-storms in August, when in Bavaria and Würtemburg there were hailstorms of exceptional violence, which in some places piled up large hailstones to a depth of a foot. Switzer-land suffered very severely from dry weather in the winter of 1920 to 1921, for early in January both the Rhine and the Rhone had shrunk to half their ordinary volume, and the general lack of water in the streams interfered with the supply of electricity. This winter in Switzerland was stated to be the driest for ninety years. The spring and early summer continued very dry, but later in the summer there was more rain. Paradoxically, the hot summer lessened the severity of the drought. The temperature exceeded 100° F. at Geneva on July 28th, and this heat melted the snow-fields and ends of the glaciers to such an extent that the snow-line receded more than 300 feet, and provided plenty of water in the rivers. The drought set in again, however, in the following winter, and the Rhine was again very low in December.

Northern Italy appears to have suffered as severely as any other part of Europe, while in the south there was plenty of rain. In the later part of the year the electric plants worked by water-power in the Swiss Alps were closed down, and in Genoa water was sold at about 2d. a gallon. In the Trentino the water of one of the lakes fell to so low a level that in December a small island appeared which had not been visible since the great drought of 1806, while in the Po valley it seems that one would have to go back to 1621 to find another drought so severe as that of 1921.

In southern Russia the drought was very severe. Western Europe generally has enough—some say too much—rainfall, and a slight deficiency is beneficial to crops, but in Russia the rainfall in a normal year is so much less than in western Europe that even a slight deficiency brings loss to the farmers. In 1921 the deficiency exceeded 25 per cent. over a large part of Southern Russia, and this caused widespread famine and many deaths.

Farther east, in Mesopotamia and Persia, there was plenty of rain, but the summer was notable for its excessive heat. In Iraq the thermometer in the shade rose above 124° F. every day for a fortnight, and on one occasion reached 129° F., while in the Persian Gulf the heat was almost unbearable. Heat, rather than excessive dryness, was the keynote of the summer in the United States and Canada also, temperature exceeding 100° F. in many parts. There were, however, an unusual number of forest fires, and the cotton crop suffered from lack of rain in the Southern United States. The area with a great deficiency of rain in Eastern Asia lay north of the main agricultural regions, in sparsely inhabited country, so that the effects of the drought were not felt so severely as in Europe.

Generally speaking, the Arctic regions had an excess of rainfall during 1921. Both deficit and excess were due to the same cause, the northward shifting of the pressure belts. The dry belt across Central Europe was due to a northward shift of the subtropical anticyclone ; the heavy rainfall of the Arctic regions was due to the northward shift of the north temperate storm belt. The excess of rainfall was greatest—more than 50 per cent.—to the north of the usual position of the Icelandic low pressure area, in two areas (heavily shaded in Fig. 11), one over North-West Iceland and the other over Northern Norway.

CHAPTER X

THE DRY YEAR 1887

" The days slip along in blue and gold and purple, and the fine white linen of the hour before dawn."—M. S. HOLLAND

IF instead of limiting our inquiry to England, we consider the British Isles as a whole, we find that the driest year on record, at least since the beginning of the nineteenth century, was undoubtedly 1887, when England, Scotland, Wales and Ireland all received less than their usual amount of rain. We have already seen that over England alone the year 1921 was drier than 1887. Over Scotland as a whole 1921 actually received about the average rainfall and the only other year, as dry as 1887 was 1870. In Ireland 1887 was by far the driest year in the series of sixty years of comparable statistics.

In any year it is the usual state of affairs for some parts of the British Isles to be appreciably wetter than usual, while others are very dry. In 1887 only a small area in the Outer Hebrides received the average rainfall, and in that year the dryness was much more widespread than in any other year. The difference between the distribution of rainfall in 1887 and 1921 is easily traced to differences in the distribution of atmospheric pressure. 1887 opened with the Icelandic low more intense than usual and a large anticyclone over most of Europe, and in February the centre of the latter moved over England, while from March to May it lay over the Atlantic to the west and north-west of Britain, bringing a long dry spell to Ireland and Western Scotland. June was typically anticyclonic over England, and July was similar to January, but from August to the end of the year the high pressure again lay to the west and north-west.

Over the nine months February to October the average pressure was as much above normal over Iceland as it was over England, and the drought combined the characteristics of anticyclonic droughts, which are most severe over Eastern England, and east wind droughts, which are more intense in the Western Highlands and Ireland. This accounts for its widespread distribution. In 1921, on the other hand, pressure was abnormally high over the southern part of the British Isles, but it was below normal over Iceland. The latter drought was a very intense example of the purely anticyclonic type and the strong south-west winds over Western Scotland brought an excess of rainfall there.

The variation in the rainfall from place to place is so irregular that instances are on record in which one station records its highest and another its lowest annual rainfall for over half a century in the same year. This happened in the four years 1875, 1880, 1897 and 1915. Thus 1915 was the driest year on record in the neighbourhood of Fort William, at the head of the Caledonian Canal, and the wettest year on record at Brighton. It has been found that during a period of sixty years more than two-thirds of them were the driest or wettest in the series at some one or more stations in the British Isles. Generally the areas with this distinction are small ; for example, 1927 was the wettest year on record only over a small area round High Wycombe, in Buckinghamshire. The year 1887, however, was the driest year when individual stations are concerned, over as much as two-fifths of the whole British Isles. In the remaining three-fifths one or other of twenty-four different years, out of the last sixty, had less rainfall than 1887.

The areas where 1887 was the driest year during the last sixty years are shown in Fig. 10. The driest years on record in other parts of the British Isles are also indicated. It will be seen that whereas 1921 was the driest year over a greater part of England than 1887, the latter year gave the least rainfall over nearly the whole of Wales, over three-quarters of Ireland, and over a quarter of Scotland, actually a greater proportion than any other year in the series. The least rain-

fall was recorded in 1887 over much of the English Lake
District and the Pennines, an area particularly rich in reservoirs for the storage of water for domestic use. The land in
this region is already almost entirely utilised by various
water supply schemes. To take an example at random, the
catchment areas for the supply of Halifax, Bradford and
Keighley join on the moors overlooking Howarth, the home
of the Brontës, while the water draining to the west of
Howarth supplies the towns of Colne, Nelson or Burnley.
The capacity of those schemes which were in operation
during 1887 was more severely taxed than in those of the
forty subsequent years. On the other hand, such schemes as
have come into operation during more recent years have not
been tried under as severe conditions as those which may
reasonably be expected to recur. The fact that there was
little shortage during 1921 is no cause for congratulation,
since we have seen that 1921 was not particularly dry in
these regions. When a local authority produces a scheme
for the appropriation of the water of a stream for purposes
of water supply, account has to be taken not only of the
amount of water likely to be required for domestic purposes,
but also the quantity of water required to be passed down
the stream in order to maintain its flow. In wet weather there
is little difficulty in maintaining the flow, and water can be
abstracted without detriment to any of the interests lower
down. In dry weather, not only is there little available water
to replenish the reservoirs, but the stored water has to be
utilised in part to maintain the flow of the stream. For this
reason the number of persons which can be supplied by any
water-works scheme depends on the water available in dry
periods as well as the storage capacity of the reservoirs.
Precise details of the rainfall of a year like 1887 are therefore of paramount importance. In the case of London the
difficulty of supplying the 7,000,000 persons in dry weather
has been overcome by building enormous reservoirs. There
is a further factor of safety in this case in that all the water
is not obtained from the River Thames and its tributary the
Lea. Large supplies, about 18 per cent. of the total, are

obtained from deep wells mainly in the Kent district, which do not depend directly on the rainfall. Thus, in the dry year 1921 there was practically no difference in the level of the water in these wells. It would be possible therefore to utilise a larger supply from this source during any period of drought. Moreover, the capacity of the fifty storage reservoirs for unfiltered water is equal to the full supply for London for as long a period as seventy-eight days. The largest reservoir at Littleton, to the north of Staines, named after Queen Mary, is four miles in circumference and probably the largest artificial reservoir of its kind in the world. It is unfortunate for the general public of London that in order to secure a large capacity this reservoir has a high retaining embankment and is consequently not generally known. In the neighbourhood of other towns the large artificial reservoirs have added much to the natural beauty of the districts and are a source of great enjoyment.

During 1887 it is on record that near Maresfield, to the south of the Ashdown Forest, threepence a pail was paid for water, while at the opposite end of England the level of Lake Derwentwater fell on July 9th to a lower level than ever previously recorded, being 8 inches below low water mark. The difficulties in the Midlands are illustrated by the following quotation, dated August 27th : " In spite of the rain which fell a week ago the people residing in Langho, near Blackburn, are suffering from water famine. All the water used has to be brought from Clitheroe by rail, in milk cans, and it is served out to the people by the station master, who allows a bucket to each family. Beyond this there is not a drop of water in the district."

In these days of more precise knowledge as to rainfall, it is essential that each water-works should pay particular attention to the quantity of rain which has fallen in previous dry years so that adequate precautions may be taken to secure a reasonable supply in the dry years of the future. It is more than probable that many existing companies have only been able to cope with the additional requirements of the increased population because of the recent long run of

wet years, and that when the inevitable run of dry years
arrives they will be compelled to obtain further supplies.
The more recently established power schemes for the utilisa-
tion of the heavy rainfall of the highlands are in a similar
manner limited by the incidence of the rainfall. Even during
August, 1887, we read that " 4,000 quarry men in North
Wales were thrown out of work owing to failure of streams
supplying the quarries. About 1,000 men were thrown out at
the Llanelly tin-works owing to the supply from the Cwm-
lleide Reservoir being obliged to be stopped." The pipe-
lines at Cwm Dyli, near the Penygwyrd Hotel at the foot
of Snowdon and at Dolgarrog are well known. Every spring
certain electrical furnaces for the production of aluminium
have to be closed down, owing partly to the smaller rainfall
of the spring months and partly to the marked loss by
evaporation in all but the winter months. The amount of
work which can be done is considerably less in dry years,
although these districts are fortunately immune from such
long periods of little or no rain as occur in the south-east
of England.

A study of the rainfall of dry years is, from this point of
view, of great importance. Treating the British Isles as a
whole, the general rainfall of each month of 1887 is shown
in Fig. 12, the monthly totals being expressed as percentages
of the thirty-five-year average of the corresponding months.
The values for 1921 are shown on the same diagram for comparison, the rainfall during these two years being naturally
similar in that most months were drier than the average.
Apart from January and March, 1921, which were both
much wetter than the corresponding months of 1887, the
falls in each month had many points of resemblance. It is
true that August was wet in 1921 and dry in 1887, but the
reverse occurred in September, and together the rainfalls
of the two months were about equal. It will be seen that
while 1921 gave us the extremely dry months of February
and June, with only 30 per cent. of the average, the year
1887 had more months of moderate dryness, with a fall of
about 70 per cent. Again, three months in 1921 were wet,

while in 1887 there was only one wet month. In short, the
drought of 1887 was more sustained over the country generally while that of 1921 was more intense locally.

While in 1921 the least rainfall recorded was 10 inches in
Kent, during 1887 the smallest totals were 13 inches, recorded
at two or three stations in the Fen District. During 1887, on
the other hand, falls of less than 20 inches were widespread
over England. They occurred in most of the country to the
east of a line from the Vale of York to Oxford, and the same
amount was recorded as far west as Hereford. Less than
20 inches also fell along parts of the South Coast, including

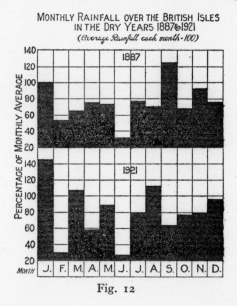

Fig. 12

the more low-lying area between Hastings and Hythe and
the neighbourhood of Selsey Bill. Outside England such
small falls were rare, although experienced near Dublin and
along the Firth of Forth and the Moray Firth. During 1887
practically 30 per cent. of the whole of England received less
than 20 inches. This is in marked contrast with the average
year, where only a part of the Thames Estuary has as little
as 20 inches. The total area with between 20 and 30 inches

was practically the same in 1887 as in the average year, although of course the actual areas were not identical. On the average more than half of England receives less than 30 inches, while in the driest year on record, 1887, this amount fell over four-fifths of the whole area.

We can make the comparison in another way. An average year finds 6·3 per cent. of the surface of England with more than 50 inches. In 1887 there was only about 1 per cent. exceeding this total. In the wettest year, 1872, more than a quarter of the whole of England received more than 50 inches. In 1887 about three-quarters of England received less than 25 inches, while in 1872 no single rain-gauge recorded so little. In Ireland the difference between the rainfall of these two years was equally remarkable. In 1872 the rainfall was everywhere more than 35 inches, while in 1887 this amount was recorded only in the mountainous districts of Kerry, Connemara, Donegal and Londonderry.

Many places recorded in 1887 less than half the amount which fell in 1872, fifteen years earlier. The values are so striking that for certain widely distributed stations the annual falls for these two extreme years are set out below.

County	Station	Rainfall	
		1887	1872
ENGLAND.		Inches	Inches
Cornwall - -	Penzance - -	27·9	57·2
Shropshire - -	Church Stretton -	23·5	55·2
Nottingham -	Nottingham - -	18·5	38·4
Cheshire - -	Altrincham - -	22·1	54·9
Yorks - -	Bradford - -	27·3	59·0
WALES, ETC.			
Pembroke - -	Haverfordwest -	35·2	69·8
Carnarvon - -	Llandudno - -	21·6	48·0
Isle of Man -	Douglas - -	27·0	62·9
IRELAND.			
Cork - - -	Cork - - -	26·4	61·6
Wexford - -	Gorey - - -	22·9	52·1
Dublin - -	Balbriggan - -	20·4	43·3

Perhaps the most striking fall is that at Altrincham, which, in 1872, received practically two and a half times as much rain as 1887.

Even in this dry year, 1887, as much as 100 inches was probably recorded in Snowdonia, the English Lake District and parts of the Western Highlands of Scotland. It will be recalled that these are the wettest areas on the average map (Fig. 2). In fact, the map of the rainfall of this dry year shows the same main features of dependence on configuration as appear in the average map. The same regions give in general the largest or smallest values on both maps, and there is a good deal of resemblance in the general distribution of wet and dry areas, although the values are everywhere so much smaller on the map for 1887.

If we were required to select a year of really good weather from the point of view of outdoor recreations we should naturally suggest 1887. The description set out below, taken from the *Letters of Mary Sibylla Holland*, and written on December 17th, 1887, clearly supports the claim of this year for consideration. " The morning is charming here—a south wind and bright ascending sun which illuminated the whole Cathedral east and south. We have had many such mornings lately." Such is our climate, however, that even this year had its delinquencies. There was a sharp frost in August, while November was unusually dull and gloomy in southern England. The meteorological observer at Diss, in Norfolk, quoted Hood's well-known description as particularly fitting November, 1887 :

> " No warmth, no cheerfulness, no healthful ease,
> No comfortable feel in any member,
> No shade, no sun, no butterflies, no bees,
> No fruits, no flowers, no leaves, no birds,
> No-vember ! "

CHAPTER XI

DRY YEARS OF THE EIGHTEENTH CENTURY

" Not as single spies, but in battalions."

IN the two preceding chapters, and also in the earlier chapters
dealing with the rainy years from 1872 to 1927, we have
expressed all the various rainfall data in terms of what we
have labelled the " standard normal " for the period 1881 to
1915. Hitherto we have not thought it necessary to explain
how that standard normal was obtained ; we have just taken
it for granted. When we go back to the first half of the
eighteenth century, however, and still compare the rainfall
measurements with the " standard normal," it is a different
matter, and some explanation does seem to be required.

In some circumstances the calculation of a standard normal
is a matter of simple arithmetic. That happens when the
rainfall records have been made at the same gauge throughout
the whole period, 1881–1915, while the " exposure " of the
gauge has not been in any way modified by the growth or
cutting down of trees or the erection of buildings, which might
cause the gauge to catch less or more rain than it otherwise
would. Thirty-five years seems a long period of time, but
there are many rain-gauges in this country which have been
maintained under similar conditions, and the rainfall regularly recorded, for longer periods than this, and sometimes
by the same observer throughout. However, it is too much
to expect that the rainfall records of the eighteenth century
should have been carried on continuously in the same localities for more than a hundred years, and in order to compile
the standard normals with which to compare these early
records, more elaborate methods were required.

There are two alternative methods, both of which are

possible. All the available " standard normals " have been plotted on large scale rainfall maps, and we can simply estimate from such a map the standard normal for the site of one of the earlier records ; such a procedure is very simple and easy, but it takes for granted that the early gauge was of a satisfactory pattern and was correctly exposed— points about which we are not always quite satisfied. The alternative method is to make use of the well-known fact that at two places which are fairly close together the pro- portionate variations of rainfall are very nearly the same. For example, consider a place A, where the " standard normal " is 50 inches a year, and the rainfall during the period 1870–79 was 55 inches, and a place B not far off, where the rainfall during the years 1870–79 was 44 inches, while we do not know the standard normal directly. During the period 1870–79 the rainfall at B was four-fifths of that at A, and we assume that the same ratio held during the period 1881–1915, so that we calculate the standard normal at B as 40 inches a year. We can use this standard normal at B to calculate that at a third station, C, which ante- dates A entirely, and so we can work back from station to station so long as our records overlap. This was the method employed by the late Mr. G. J. Symons, who first calculated the rainfall of England year by year back to 1726. It is quite satisfactory so long as the available records are really good and free from error, but it is subject to the difficulty that an error introduced at any point (for example, by the growth of a tree near the rain-gauge) affects the figures, calculated as percentages of the standard normal, for all previous years. Thus the figures calculated by Symons were to some extent spoilt by the growth of a holly bush near the rain-gauge at Exeter, and his early percentages were rather lower than they should have been.

The observations have recently been critically re- examined, and revised figures were published in the *Meteoro- logical Magazine* for February, 1928. In making this revision, the two alternative methods described above were combined in such a way as to retain as far as possible the advantages of both without their difficulties. For most of the second quarter of the nineteenth century, there are only two long rainfall records, at Plymouth and at Lyndon in Rutland, but experiments have shown that records from two stations, if they are suitably placed, as these were, give a very good idea of the variations of rainfall in England from year to year.

The earliest rainfall record known in this country was commenced in 1677 by Mr. Townley at Townley in Lancashire, and extended with some breaks until 1704. Another record, at Upminster in Essex, was maintained continuously from 1697 to 1716 by W. Derham, the same Fellow of the Royal Society whose opinions on the cause of tidal floods were quoted in Chapter VII. After 1716 there is a break, and no further observations are known until 1726, when a record commences at Southwick, near Oundle, in Northants. The early records at Townley and at Upminster, therefore, cannot be connected directly with the later ones, and we do not know enough about the gauges and exposures to compare the figures directly with normals estimated from the rainfall map. But though we have no actual measurements of rain during these intervening years, we possess several careful weather diaries compiled without the aid of instruments. From these diaries it has proved possible to make estimates of the rainfall of England which are about as near to the true figure as we should get if we had one centrally placed rainfall station. The method was to give each month a numerical figure based on the following scale : + 4, exceptionally rainy ; + 3, very rainy ; + 2, rainy ; + 1, rather rainy ; 0, normal ; − 1, rather dry ; − 2, dry ; − 3, very dry. The figures for the twelve months were added up and the annual totals were found to range from about + 20 to − 18. Comparison of similar estimates for the years 1727 to 1800 with the rainfall measurements for England shows that these would correspond with rainfalls of 140 per cent. and 64 per cent. of normal respectively. This non-instrumental series of rainfall estimates could then be used like a rainfall record to connect the series of measurements at Townley and Upminster with the later series commencing in 1726, and so extend our series of percentage estimates back to 1677.

The most remarkable point brought out by these figures is the dryness of the first half of the eighteenth century. The ten-year means, expressed as percentages of the standard normal for 1881 to 1915 over England as a whole, are as follows :

1701–10	1711–20	1721–30	1731–40	1741–50
94	95	98	92	87

Every decade was drier than the standard normal, and the last decade, with only 87 per cent. of the normal, was outstandingly dry ; in fact, during the sixty years 1868–1927 only eight isolated years had a smaller amount. The driest period extended from 1737 to 1750 inclusive ; the average rainfall of these fourteen years was only 87 per cent. of the standard normal, and the total deficiency was almost equal to the rainfall of two average years.

The first of the outstanding dry years of the eighteenth century occurred in 1714 ; it appears also to have been one of the worst. The rain-gauge at Upminster in this year recorded the astonishingly low figure of 11·25 inches, which is almost the smallest total ever recorded by a rain-gauge in this country. In fact it stood as a record until 1921, when an amount of rather less than 10 inches fell in the extreme east of Kent. The annual average for W. Derham's gauge at Upminster, corrected to the standard normal for the period 1881–1915 by means of the non-instrumental record described above, is 22 inches, so that the rainfall in that part of Essex in 1714 was little more than half the normal.

Unfortunately the details of Derham's measurements have not been preserved, but from the various notes and non-instrumental weather diaries which we have it seems very doubtful whether any month of the year exceeded its average for the period 1881–1915. The driest months appear to have been January, May, June, August, and November. The drought apparently extended over a large part of England and Ireland, but was not noted as severe in Scotland, so that it was presumably of the normal anticyclonic type. Taking into account all the available information, the rainfall over England as a whole is estimated as about 56 per cent. of the standard normal, less than five-sixths of that of 1921 with 69 per cent.

The next event was a spell of four dry years, 1730, 1731, 1732 and 1733, all of which, together with the first half of 1734, had a rainfall considerably below normal. Of these years the driest was 1731, with a general rainfall over England of 66 per cent. of the standard normal, or 3 per cent. below 1921. Like so many of these dry years, it opened with a great frost and some snow, but the summer was hot, especially September, which was also exceptionally dry. During the succeeding two years the springs failed in many places. The summer of 1733 was very hot, especially June in the Midlands (relieved by a great thunderstorm with hail on June 27th), and July in London. Autumn also was fine and warm. The drought did not break until June 12th, 1734.

The latter half of 1734 was very wet, and that year as a whole stands out as a wet year ; 1735 and 1736 were also wetter than usual, but with 1737 began a series of fourteen years of which ten were dry, one normal and only three wet. The worst spell came in 1740–43, exactly ten years after the dry spell of 1730–33. In the latter the average rainfall over England was 82 per cent. of the standard normal ; the average during the drought of 1740–43 was only 73 per cent., this four-year average actually being less than the figure for the single year 1887, which before the coming of 1921 was noted for its droughtiness.

The drought began, as usual, with a frost. The Thames was frozen over in December, 1739, and a famous frost-fair was held on the river from Christmas Day of that year until February 17th, 1740. A printing-press was set up on the ice, on which mementoes of the great frost were printed ; another press was set up on the Ouse at York. The winter, besides being exceptionally cold, was very dry ; there were

K

" not three hours continued rain from the beginning of November until the following April." It is recorded in White's " Selborne " that " the cold north-east winds continued to blow through April and May." The drought continued with unabated severity until the end of July, and in these seven months only 6·9 inches fell at Plymouth, or 45 per cent. of normal. At Lyndon, Rutland, 1·8 inches fell in the first four months, the contribution of February being 0·06 inch, and less than 4 inches more until near the end of July, when there occurred a terrific downpour, 2½ inches falling in twelve hours. The drought was also very severe in Ireland ; it was of the east wind type, and at times the wind rose to a considerable force. A few days after Christmas much damage was done to the shipping in the Thames, and the cold, dry, cutting winds of spring could hardly be paralleled. Snow fell in Yorkshire on April 22nd, and the high, cool winds continued until the end of July.

The latter half of 1740 was rather rainy, and a fairly good harvest was secured. It may be noted that on November 1st London was visited by a " dreadful hurricane," which lasted from 6 to 11 p.m., during which one of the spires of Westminster Abbey was blown down. The winter of 1740–41 was cold and rather dry, while the spring was again excessively dry, especially March, April and May, only relieved by some showers about the middle of May. Symons describes the weather from the beginning of January to the first week of June as " almost one continued drought." At Plymouth the total of these three months was only 1·4 inches, at Lyndon only 1·3 inches. The break in June was only partial, and the weather continued through the summer very hot and rather dry, with a little rain now and then. July had less than an inch at both Plymouth and Lyndon. There was a plentiful supply of rain in the first half of September, the amount at Lyndon totalling 4½ inches by the 19th ; from then on to the end of the year the weather was mild and pleasant, with rather less than the normal rainfall, except in November, which was wet and cold. December was dry, with less than half an inch at Lyndon. The year as a whole was slightly wetter than 1731 (67 compared with 66 per cent. of normal over England as a whole), but has not since been equalled for drought in this country, not even by 1921.

1742 began with heavy snow in the north, but the greater part of January was mild and fairly rainy. February, March and April were dry and cold, especially March, during which month both Plymouth and Lyndon were practically rainless. The rest of the year had rains, except for a very dry August, and autumn was cold and wet. The year closed with three weeks of very severe frost without snow. The year as a whole had 80 per cent. of the standard normal rainfall over England, so that while dry it was not excessively droughty.

1743 was again a very dry year, with 69 per cent. of the standard normal for England, a degree of drought which has not since been exceeded, though it was equalled in 1788 and 1921. The chief feature of the year was the very dry weather of May, June, August and September, the last month having only one-quarter of an inch at Plymouth and only one-hundredth at Lyndon. July, while only moderately wet at Plymouth, was very rainy at Rutland, the total of 5·23 inches being by far the greatest July total during the whole period from 1737 to 1750, and only exceeded in any month by August, 1737.

The remaining years of the 1740's were not especially noteworthy, averaging only 4 per cent. below the standard normal, but 1750, the last of the series, received only three-quarters of the normal fall, and with the single exception of 1788, was the driest year until 1887. Both 1749 and 1750 were years with a marked anticyclonic distribution of rain-fall, for Plymouth, with 34 inches in each year, received almost its normal complement, while Lyndon, with only 16 inches, points to a deficiency of rain in the central parts of the country. 1749 was especially dry at Lyndon, receiv-ing only a quarter of an inch more than the very dry year 1741. A record which began at Norwich in 1750 shows that

that year was dry in East Anglia also, the total being only 20 inches. 1750 was unusual, however, in that the drought was not confined to any particular series of months, but the deficit of rainfall was spread almost evenly over the whole year. If one had to pick out any season for especial praise, one would select the autumn, which was remarkably fine and warm in London.

The dryness of the first half of the eighteenth century was so marked and persistent as almost to constitute a different climate from that of the last half of the nineteenth and the beginning of the twentieth centuries. It extended to the continent of Europe, for a long record at Paris shows that the rainfall of that city was abnormally light from 1721 to 1750. In percentages of the average for a long period of 150 years we have, for 1711 to 1720, 97 per cent. ; 1721 to 1730, 79 per cent. ; 1731 to 1740, 86 per cent., and 1741 to 1750, 88 per cent., the mean of the last three decades being 84 per cent. compared with 89 per cent. (of the standard normal) over England. The earliest years of a long record which began in 1748 at Lund in Sweden also point to a rainfall well below the normal. In connection with the drought of 1731 in France we cannot forbear to quote the following extract from " The Civil and Religious History of Vatan (Indre) ": " The winter of this year 1731 did not begin until February 2nd ; it was very prolonged and very severe ; snow was on the ground for six weeks and following on this cold, there was a persistent drought. Intercession to Saint Laurian was made this year for better weather, and for this a public procession was held on April 26th, in which more than 60 parishes in the neighbourhood took part. The parish of Issoudun, with its noblemen, were there. Next day, their prayers were answered and it rained so heavily that the harvest was washed away, and was so to speak, hopeless."

CHAPTER XII

HISTORIC DROUGHTS OF THE MIDDLE AGES

" It is strange what weather we have had."
                                    PEPYS

THE subject of historic droughts is figuratively as well as
literally drier than that of historic rains, because while the
latter are diversified by chronicles of storm and flood, droughts
are essentially without incident, and it is difficult to make
this chapter much more than a catalogue of dates. The
greater part of the following material is based on a compilation by the late G. J. Symons, the founder of the study of
British rainfall, which appeared in *British Rainfall* for 1887.
The earliest record of a drought in this country refers to
A.D. 298, when a great drought and famine occurred in
Wales ; it thus follows the earliest record of a flood by
nearly three centuries. The second comes in 362, the
third in 374, and from thence onwards droughts are recorded
at intervals of from forty to a hundred years, more or less
until 676 : 439 ; 480 (in Scotland), and 484 (the latter
described as drying up all springs and rivers) ; 589, 605
(with scorching heat). In 676 began a series of great
droughts which recurred annually for six or seven years,
and probably mark the low-water mark in the rainfall of
England, at least until the first half of the eighteenth century.
The culminating point of this dry spell was marked by a
picturesque incident, which was recorded by the Venerable
Bede in his " Ecclesiastical History of England," Book IV,
chapter 13 : " But Bishop Wilfrid, while preaching the
Gospel to the people [the South Saxons, A.D. 681], not only
delivered them from the misery of eternal damnation, but
also from a terrible calamity of temporal death. For no rain

had fallen in that district for three years before his arrival
in the province, whereupon a grievous famine fell upon the
people and pitilessly destroyed them. . . . But on the very
day on which the nation received the Baptism of the faith,
there fell a soft but plentiful rain, the earth revived, the
fields grew green again, and the season was pleasant and
fruitful." From the locality where the drought was most
severely felt, it was evidently of the anticyclonic type, but
although such anticyclones are sometimes very persistent,
we must suspect that the duration and intensity of the
drought were somewhat exaggerated by the chronicler. The
drought of 298, from its occurrence in Wales, a country
of orographic rainfall, and that of 605, with its scorching
heat (compare 1911), were probably of the east wind type.

The dry period in the latter half of the seventh century
seems to have ended in 682, but another long series of dry
years began in 713, no fewer than fifteen severe droughts
being recorded by the annalists between that year and 775,
or nearly one year in four. As a rule details are wanting, but
now and again we are vouchsafed some illuminating side-
lights. The series runs : 713, 717 (a dry summer ; both
years in Ireland), 721 (very hot summer), 737, 741, 743
("burning drought "; there was also an earthquake), 744
(Ireland), 747 and 748 (both in Ireland), 759 (associated with
a great frost from October 1st, 759, to February 26th, 760 ;
this drought was also severe in Ireland), 762 (long and
terrible drought with heat), 763 (summer so hot that the
springs dried up), and 764. The latter year included a
" marvellous great snow and so extreme a frost as the like
had not been heard of, continuing from the beginning of
the winter almost to the midst of the spring," and the drought
followed immediately on the frost. The drought of 772
occurred in Ireland, that of 775 was associated with excessive
heat, and as in 760, followed a long frost. Most of these
droughts, both from the extremes of temperature which
accompanied them and from the frequency with which they
were severely felt in Ireland, seem to have been of the east
wind type.

In strong contrast with the eighth century, the ninth produced only one record of a notable drought, that of 822-3, of long duration and most severe in England, and so presumably of the anticyclonic type. Then follows a gap of 165 years before the next series, which began in 987 and was especially notable for the great heat which accompanied the dryness : 987, 988, 989, 992, 993 and 994 (summers so hot that the corn and fruit dried up). The drought of 1006 came in winter and spring, but that of 1009, in Ireland, again gave a burning summer. In 1022 the heat was so excessive that men and animals died ; the fame of this " prodigious drought " penetrated into France and Germany. Then followed a gap of fifty-five years, after which, in 1077, came a single dry summer, of which we have no further particulars, and in 1086 a " horrible drought."

The next group began in 1102, with a summer drought accompanied by excessive heat. The winter of 1113-14 and the greater part of the latter year were excessively dry, and it seems that this must rank as one of the outstanding droughts which occur only half a dozen times in a thousand years, like 680-81, and the subsequent droughts of 1241 and 1252-53, 1591-92, and 1714. As early as April 14th the Thames was almost without water, and the summer was so hot and dry that corn and forests took fire. The drought was prolonged into the autumn, and early in October the Thames again ran so dry that for two days children waded across between the bridges and the town. On October 6th the Medway also was almost dry. It must be remembered that at that time the Thames had not been embanked, and the tide, not confined within narrow channels, did not run so deep as at present, nor scour the river bed. Both from the fact that it was most severe in South-East England, and from its remarkable persistence, we may infer that the drought of 1114 was of the anticyclonic type. In 1122 all three spring months were dry and hot. The summers of 1129, 1130 and 1131 were all hot and dry, the drought being excessive in Ireland in the first year. 1135 was again excessively dry and hot, almost rivalling 1114 ; woods, grass and corn were

burnt, and rivers dried up. The drought continued during
1136 and 1137, and in the latter year the rivers again ran
dry, while in 1144 it is recorded that there was a great drought
all harvest and long after. The year 1149 had a dry winter,
and this ended a remarkable period of forty-seven years, of
which thirteen included droughts sufficiently severe to be
put on record by our annalists, while 1114 seems to have
been really phenomenal, and 1135 was not far behind.

The second half of the twelfth century was less notable.
A drought quoted by Symons in 1152 is so suspiciously
similar in its details to that of 1252 that we suspect an
error of a hundred years. Sir Richard Gregory records that
in 1157 the Thames was crossed with dry feet, but no details
are available. In 1173 the winter and spring were extraordinarily fine until nearly the end of May, and in 1177
there was so great a drought in summer that there was no
harvest. After that we have no further records of drought
until 1222, when late-sown corn died. In 1224 there was a
drought in winter. Symons quotes Matthew Paris's Chronicle
that in the summer of 1236, " after a winter beyond measure
rainy . . . a constant drought, attended by an almost unendurable heat, succeeded, which lasted four months or
more. The marshes and lakes were dried up to their very
bottoms, water-mills stood uselessly still—the water being
dried up ; and the earth gaped with numerous fissures ;
the corn, too, in a great many places, scarcely grew to the
height of two feet. . . ." Another series began in 1240
with a three months' drought. This was the year that Amicia,
Countess of Devon, brought water for domestic purposes
five miles to Tiverton, one of the earliest attempts on record
since Roman times for mitigating the effects of prolonged
droughts. The next year, 1241, commenced with a heavy fall
of snow, followed by a frost. After this Symons records that
" from March 25th to October 28th continuous dryness and
incomparable heat dried up deep lakes and extensive marshes,
drained many rivers, parched up the warrens and suspended
the working of mills ; hence the pastures withered away,
herbage died, and consequently the flocks and herds pined

away with hunger and thirst." The drought returned in 1243 and continued during 1244 ; it broke in the middle of November of the latter year, when " great thunder and lightning chanced with a marvellous intemperate season for the space of 15 days together."

1252 gives a record of what was very likely the most intense east wind drought of the past thousand years. Symons quotes from Matthew Paris's Chronicle that " during most of March, and the whole of April and May, the earth was parched by the burning heat of the sun, the wind continually blowing from the east, north or north-east. . . . The sun rising to its solstitial height in the heavens, its immoderate and unendurable heat so burnt up the surface of the earth that all the herbage was withered, and the meadows refused all kinds of food to the cattle." Miss Ormerod's manuscript volume gives further details : " On the 13th day of March began a sore drought. . . . The grass was so burned up in pastures and meadows, that if a man took up some of it in his hands it straight fell to powder, and so cattle were starved for lack of meat. And because of the exceeding hot nights there was such abundance of fleas, flies and gnats that people were vexed and brought in case to be weary of their lives. And herewith chanced many diseases, as sweats, agues and other. In the harvest time fell there a great dearth and murrain amongst cattle, and especially in Norfolk, in the Fens and other parts of the south. This infection was such that dogs and ravens feeding on the dead carrion, swelled straightway and died, so that the people durst eat no beef lest the flesh haply might be infected." This drought continued all through the months of April, May, June and July, " when there followed good plenty of rain." Lowe records that there were " great tempests upon the sea and fearfull," but we do not know whether this refers to the period of the drought or to the break which came in August and September. In October the drought set in again, and apparently continued into or through November, but in the absence of any mention of east winds this return of dry weather may have been of the anticyclonic rather than of the east wind type. The winter months of 1252 to 1253 do not seem to have been abnormal, but the drought returned in the spring and summer of the latter year. It broke again at just the wrong time, for, as Symons quotes from Miss Ormerod, " in the harvest season fell such wet that great floods, by the rising of the rivers and overflow of their banks, did much hurt in sundry places of the realm." The break was, however, only temporary, and did not make up for the previous shortage, for " again in the latter end of the harvest about Michaelmas, there was eftsoon such a drought that men could get no grinding at the mills, but were constrained to go in some places a day's journey off to get their corn ground." Evidently the heavy rains of August ran quickly off the hardened ground into the rivers, and failed to replenish the deep springs. We should not be accused of extravagance if we were to claim these two years, 1252 and 1253, as the driest consecutive two years since the beginning of history in this country. Their chief rival to this distinction are the years of St. Wilfrid's drought, 680–1, of which we have unfortunately too few details to say much.

This was not the end of the series of droughts. 1254 began with a long and severe frost, and the autumn and winter of that year were continually stormy, but then in 1255 followed a long spell of dry northerly winds, which began in the middle of March and continued through the whole of April and May. There was no rain during April, and it is recorded that the dry winds " altogether stopped the dews of morning and checked those of evening," thus greatly intensifying the severity of the drought. Later in the year, however, there came abundance of rain, so heavy and continuous " that marvellous floods followed thereupon." After an interval of three years, a moderate drought occurred in 1259, followed by one of much greater severity in 1260, when, according to reports quoted by Symons, no rain fell all the year until August. Ireland experienced a summer drought in 1262, and Eastern England in 1267. The years 1276 to 1278 brought long, hot and dry summers, that of 1277 being associated with a scarcity of fodder, but probably there was nothing exceptional. In 1281 it is recorded that there was so great a drought that men passed over the Thames dry shod between Westminster and Lambeth, and over the Medway between Strood and Rochester. 1285 was again dry and hot, diversified by one of our great London thunderstorms, and in 1288 or 1289 the heat was so intense that many persons died. Summer droughts occurred in 1291, 1293 (the latter very hot following on snow in May), and 1294.

Mr. G. M. Meyer, in an interesting study of the history of water-mills in East Kent, published in the *Quarterly Journal of the Royal Meteorological Society* for October, 1927, has brought forward evidence for a decrease of rainfall about 1275. It appears that about 1150 there were as many as twelve water-mills in the neighbourhood of Canterbury, while about 1550 the number had decreased to five. As early as the reign of Henry II the monks of Christ Church complained of the lack of water for their mills, but a number of lawsuits and other documents indicate that the shortage became acute in the latter half of the thirteenth century, and that the rainfall about 1303 was much less than in 1217.

The early summer of 1300 was especially dry in Cornwall, and 1321, 1324 and 1325 all had dry summers. The latter year is somewhat wordily described in Miss Ormerod's collection : " The summer this year proved exceedingly hot and dry, so that springs and rivers failed to yield their accustomed course of waters, by reason whereof great numbers of cattle and beasts, both wild and tame, died through want of convenient liquor to assuage their vehement thirst." This drought apparently extended into 1326. Symons' entry for 1345 is curious : " Called ' the dry summer ' as from March to the end of April little or no rain fell." Even allowing for the fact that the calendar was then more than a week behind the present calendar, the dates hardly seem to fit the description.

After this the entries became very numerous, and will not be referred to individually ; it will suffice to mention a few curious or outstanding events. The droughts and heat of 1473, 1474 and 1475 were attributed to the two comets of

1472. In 1540, following on the dry year 1539, rain fell only six times between February and September 19th. The next year, 1541, was even drier ; the Trent, at Nottingham, diminished to a straggling brook, and the Thames was so low " that the sea water even at ebb extended beyond London Bridge."

In 1591 Sir Francis Drake brought water from Dartmoor to Plymouth by means of a channel 24 miles in length, which can still be seen. The need for such a work was presumably due to the growth in the population of Plymouth rather than to a dry spell, however, for, though both 1590 and 1591 were relatively dry, there are no records of any outstanding droughts in the period preceding the construction of the channel.

The New River, supplying London with water, was commenced some eighteen years later. The source is at the Chadwell Spring, near Ware, and this artificial channel (constructed by Sir Hugh Myddelton) was originally 38 miles long, although subsequently it has been considerably shortened. London receives annually some twenty thousan million gallons from this source.

The year 1592 presents an unusual case in that, following a severe spring drought, summer was a period of strong westerly winds, which nevertheless brought little rain in central and eastern England. The Trent and other rivers were almost dried up and the Thames was so low that it could be crossed on horseback at London Bridge. We may presume that the Azores anticyclone increased in intensity and moved some distance to the north-east, so that its northern extremity lay close to southern England, but that the Icelandic low suffered no change of position or intensity. In these circumstances depressions would pass rapidly along the main track to the north of Scotland, but would resemble the Channel type, without secondaries on their southern flank, rather than the usual north of Scotland type. The westerly winds would be strong, but very stable, and though there was probably a good deal of orographic rain on the western highlands, there would be little cyclonic rain in England or Ireland.

1614 was another example of a hot, dry summer following a very severe winter. At York it began to snow and freeze on January 16th, and the frost continued unbroken, with occasional snow, until March 7th, by which time the depth of snow was greater than in any other year within living memory. When the thaw came there was a great flood, but without rain, and the drought continued until August 20th, causing a great scarcity of hay and corn. This drought was experienced also over a wide area throughout Europe.

In 1652 there was a very severe drought in spring and summer, the latter season being described as the driest ever known in Scotland. The heat was excessive, but on June 25th the drought was temporarily broken in London by a violent thunderstorm, with hail and strong winds. During the course of the summer also there was a great storm off the Shetlands. The drought was probably due to an anticyclone centred over Scandinavia and extending its influence over the British Isles, a condition which not infrequently occurs in winter and especially spring, and which is occasionally seen in summer.

Rainfall observations began in this country in 1677 at Townley, in Lancashire, but the first notable drought which these observations show is in 1681. These early records cannot be connected directly with the continuous series which began in 1726, but an estimate has been made of the average rainfall which would have been recorded by the Townley gauge had it been in operation during the standard period, 1881 to 1915 (see p. 142), and the amount recorded in 1681 was only 76 per cent. of this normal, or just over three-fourths. This is borne out by notes from other parts of the country. Evelyn's diary records :

> June 4th (new style).—" There had scarce fallen any rain since Christmas."
> June 22nd.—" It still continued so great a drought as had never been known in England."

The Rector's Book of Clayworth, Notts :

> June 18th.—" Barley found dry in ye fields, having lain so, ever since sowing time."

and in the summary of the year :

> " It was a very dry and droughty year fro ye beging of April
> [the Rector's year began on April 1st, old style] to ye 20th June,
> not having raynd, except on ye 7th of May.   But after Xtmas
> fell abundance of rain, such as drove us out of Parson-Hern."

1684 was almost equally dry, with only 79 per cent. of the
standard normal at Townley. Evelyn's remarks are almost a
repetition of those in 1681 ; a note on July 23rd (new style)
is reminiscent of conditions during 1921 : " Some small
sprinkling of rain ; the leaves dropping from the trees as in
autumn." Clayworth records a thunderstorm on August 7th,
but the drought did not really break until August 20th, when
Evelyn notes that " we have now rain after such a drought
as no man in England had known," while at Clayworth,
August 22nd to 31st were rainy.

1691 was even worse, Townley's rainfall being only 72 per
cent. of normal, or less than three-quarters. In this year,
however, spring and early summer were moderately rainy,
while late summer was dry, autumn was, to quote Evelyn,
" an extraordinary dry and hot season," and winter was
" exceeding dry and calm ; no rain for many months past."

These dry years of the latter half of the seventeenth
century, which come in such rapid succession, probably
form part of the same long dry period which included the
first half of the eighteenth century, and which was described
in the preceding chapter.

PART III

VARIATIONS OF RAINFALL

EXTREMES OF RAINFALL

" This restless world
Is full of chances, which by habit's power
To learn to bear is easier than to shun."
                                                        ARMSTRONG

WHEN engineers are building a bridge over a mountain torrent, or constructing a drain, or a reservoir, or, in fact, engaged on any work the scale of which depends on the amount of rain which is likely to fall in a given time, they have to take chances. It would be possible to build a bridge so tall and strong that not once in ten thousand years would the waters of the stream beneath rise high enough to threaten its existence, but the cost of such a bridge might be excessive, and the security might be bought at too high a price. This is true even when the safety of human life is in question, for the life of each of us has its price. On the other hand, to adopt too low a standard is to invite disaster, and the wise engineer has to balance probability delicately against possibility, and to seek the solution which will give a reasonable degree of safety at a reasonable cost.

Reliable statistics of rainfall are of so recent a growth that even a hundred years ago this process was dangerously akin to guessing. For example, in building one of the bridges which were afterwards destroyed by the Moray floods, the engineers had very little exact information, and when the " oldest inhabitant " supplied details of the enormous heights to which the mountain stream had risen in earlier days, they regarded the information as incredible. Had these statements not been dismissed as senile exaggeration, the bridges would have been raised to a greater height and might have been saved.

The designer of surface drains must consider the probable magnitude of intense falls. The pure water which is brought to our houses, in the case of London by the Metropolitan Water Board, gives a more or less uniform flow in the sewers. Naturally there is a greater quantity during the day than at night, but the London County Council, who are concerned with the purification and the return of the water to the River Thames, know precisely the quantity with which they will have to deal. It is a very different problem with the " storm water," which results from heavy storms of rain, since it is much more erratic. The difficulty of dealing effectively with these heavy rains in short periods is aggravated in towns, where the rain water runs off rapidly from the roads, pavements and roofs of houses.

The methods of dealing with these two types of surplus water are naturally different, and it may not be without interest to refer briefly to those adopted in London. Originally the sewers were utilized for surface drainage alone, and up to 1815 it was a penal offence to discharge offensive matter into them. Naturally the earliest sewers were the tributaries of the River Thames and artificial open sewers which ran down the streets. These gradually became fouled by discharges from cesspools, which overflowed consequent upon the introduction of the water-closet in or about 1810. By 1847 it became compulsory to discharge all offensive matter into closed sewers. The enormous undertakings which have gradually grown up collect the sewage of London into two main sewers, which run parallel to the Thames for a long distance, joining it below Woolwich. The sewers are arranged so that the water flows seawards by gravity, and at intervals the level is raised by huge pumps, where some 500 tons per minute is raised to the height of 20 feet. At the outfalls the sludge is separated and pumped into vessels holding 1,000 tons each, which deposit it out at sea in the Black Deep.

The storm water is pumped into the Thames at a greater number of places. Among the pumping stations for this purpose may be mentioned those at Hammersmith and Lots Road (near the Electric Power Station) to the north of the river, and at Heathwell (to the east of Battersea Park), and Shad Thames (in Bermondsey), to the south of the main river. In addition to these pumping stations, there are storm relief sewers which can discharge by gravitation. Some of these tidal outlets are below the level of high water and are not available at that time.

An important factor therefore in the amount of damage caused by any intense rain is the height of the water at the time in the adjacent river or sea. An example of this is afforded by the flooding at Eastbourne on Sunday, July 16th, 1893. It rained heavily all the morning and when people came out of church they found the streets impassable. In several of the principal streets, such as Terminus Road, the water was up to the knees. The corporation had just expended £25,000 on a new surface water drainage system in which the water was stored in a large tank, and this flood coming immediately afterwards caused considerable excitement in the town, such extensive damage being unprecedented. It was high tide at midday, and the outlet of the tank was stopped by the incoming tide, so that the drains, becoming full, overflowed in the lower eastern and central portions of the town under pressure from the water entering them at the higher parts to the west and north. It is true that the rainfall was unusually heavy, since as much as 1·26 inch was recorded in an hour, but the damage would probably have been inappreciable if the rain had fallen at low tide.

Another important factor in this connection is the state of saturation of the ground. Statistics illustrating this point have recently been placed on record by the Government of Czecho-Slovakia. During a very intense fall of about one hour's duration, which occurred in Bohemia on August 11th, 1925, the total run-off was found to be only one-tenth of the rainfall. This loss was due to evaporation, absorption by the vegetation and the fairly dry state of the ground. It is obvious, therefore, that an intense fall occurring after steady rain is likely to cause much greater damage than a similar storm at the close of a hot summer afternoon. Another fact brought out by the detailed investigation made of this disastrous storm was that the maximum height attained by the River Elbe often fell short of that which might have been expected from the rainfall. The tributaries which make up the Elbe are of varying length and the water falling on the gathering grounds in the same storm was spread over a considerable interval by the time it reached the main river. Hence, instead of a single flood crest there was a series of waves following one another down the river. Then the bigger the catchment area the greater the chance of part of it missing the intense rains which are usually so local. We have the following general rule, that the larger the area of heavy rain the smaller the maximum discharge per square mile of area. In Bavaria, where the intense falls are comparable to those of this country, it is considered that an area of six square miles is likely to give a maximum discharge of 4,100 gallons per second per square mile, while an area of thirty square miles is likely to give a maximum discharge of only half this amount per square mile.

Although the flooding associated with intense falls does not depend entirely on the rainfall, it is obvious that without unusual storms there would be no flooding, so that the rainfall at these times deserves special mention. Fortunately, in this country, extremely heavy or " torrential " rain does not usually last very long. A fall of half an inch in 10 minutes is naturally less remarkable than a fall of 1 inch in 20 minutes. In fact, judging from the large number of observations which are available, it may be said that a fall of 1 inch in 1 hour is as unusual as that of half an inch in 10 minutes. A comparison of the intensities of heavy falls is facilitated by the following table of falls " worthy of notice," adopted in *British Rainfall*, which are as follows :

LIMITS OF FALLS " WORTHY OF NOTICE "

Time	Amount	Rate per hour
minutes	inches	inches
6	0·20	2·00
10	0·30	1·80
30	0·70	1·40
60	1·00	1·00
120	1·23	·61

When we consider that it may rain steadily for the greater part of a day without the rain-gauge recording half an inch these limits may appear intolerant. Actually, however, over the British Isles generally about thirty-five falls exceeding these limits are recorded every year, and as these intense falls are invariably confined to very small areas there is no doubt that many go unrecorded and the actual number is quite likely to be twice as large. At Camden Square (London), owing to the constant use of a self-recording gauge, it is possible to give the precise frequency for thirty-two years. During this period there were twenty-seven intense falls of an hour or less, which exceeded the limits for falls " worthy of notice." Such falls may therefore occur in London about once a year. Some account must necessarily be taken of the likelihood of their occurrence. One of the most intense storms on record for London was that of the great thunderstorm of June 23rd, 1878, when 3·28 inches fell in two showers lasting in all 57 minutes, but separated by a spell of half an hour with no rain. In one spell of 30 minutes 2·34 inches was recorded. Observations were generally made at half-minute intervals, and in one and a half minutes 0·26 inch fell, which is a rate of 10 inches an hour. Very few cases are on record in the British Isles of a fall exceeding this rate. The most remarkable was that at Preston, Lancashire, on August 10th, 1893. The observer actually measured 2·09 inches in 35 minutes, but on allocating this fall arrived at the conclusion that during the most intense portion of the storm 1·25 inch of rain and hail fell in five minutes, a rate of 15 inches an hour. This storm caused damage to the extent of many thousands of pounds. The greatest fall of one hour's duration which has been recorded in any part of the British Isles is about 3½ inches ; the greatest fall in half an hour about 3 inches ; the greatest in 20 minutes about 2 inches ; and the greatest in 5 minutes about 1 inch. Over the whole world the heaviest known fall in a short period is 2·47 inches in 3 minutes, at Porto Bello on May 1st, 1908.

Sewerage works intended to cope with the heaviest rainfall in the shortest time that is likely to occur, should be constructed on the basis of the greatest intensity of rain that has hitherto been recorded. The element of frequency is, however, very important in such circumstances, for it might be considered better economy to run the risk of a rainfall occurring once in fifty years in such volume as to overtax the pipes, than to spend a very large sum of money in providing a system large enough to carry off any fall that may occur in the particular locality. A good illustration of this difficulty of cost is afforded by the flooding which occurred on July 11th, 1927, in the Hammersmith, Kensington and Fulham Districts, as a result of intense thunderstorm rains during the afternoon. Actually a new scheme for the better disposal of surplus water was in operation which had just been completed at a cost of no less than £2,500,000. At Kensington 1 inch of rain fell in 12 minutes, and at Balham 1½ inches in 18 minutes, giving an intensity probably greater than ever before recorded in London for so long a time, and which may not occur again for a century.

These intense rains are usually associated with the thunderstorms of the summer, and about two-thirds of the total number on record occurred in the three months, June, July and August. There are fewer in the spring than in the autumn. Usually the precipitation takes the form of rain or hail, frequently both. One intense fall on record for the winter deserves special comment, since it took the form of snow. Usually snow is relatively widespread and persistent, and yields only a small quantity of water, but at Chepstow, on March 24th, 1888, some of the flakes were like plates, being nearly 4 inches in diameter, although only a quarter of an inch thick. Two inches of this snow fell in two minutes, and it was computed by Mr. E. J. Lowe, F.R.S., that this quantity was equivalent to 0·33 inch of water, giving a rate of nearly 10 inches an hour.

Having regard to the smaller number of observers in Scotland and Ireland than in England, it is probable that the frequency of occurrence of these intense falls of a duration of two hours or less is more comparable with that in England and Wales than is generally supposed. The most intense of these falls are undoubtedly more frequent in the Midlands and east and are associated with the summer thunderstorm of convectional origin. There is, however, a marked difference between the intense falls of the summer in the south-east of England and those of the autumn and winter in the mountainous regions of Scotland and Ireland. In the former region they are usually of short duration, while in the latter they are typically cyclonic, that is, heavy rain continuing for at least an hour or two.

So far our attention has been directed entirely to falls of two hours' duration or less, which are so productive of local flooding. Falls of longer duration are also liable to cause considerable flooding, since they are often more widespread. In the case of daily falls much more information is available, since most gauges are read at 9 a.m. every morning. The heavy falls in short periods already referred to have either been recorded by automatic gauges or by observers who have made readings before and after the heavy rain. In the case of daily readings a rough guide as to whether a fall is worthy of notice or not is given by the practice adopted in *British Rainfall*, of mentioning specially only such falls which reach or exceed either an amount of 2·5 inches, or a proportion of 7·5 per cent. of the total for that year. By using the double criterion it is possible to pick out falls which are noteworthy when judged by the standard appropriate for the dry districts, as well as to the falls which would be remarkable anywhere. In any year the largest of the daily falls are usually found in normally wet mountainous regions in the west of the country, while the largest percentage falls occur most frequently in central and eastern districts. The former are evidently the result of orographical influences, while the latter are usually associated with summer thunderstorms, which, as is well known, most frequently occur inland.

A fall of more than 3 inches in one day has been recorded in every county of Great Britain, except Clackmannan and Kinross, but in Ireland eight out of the thirty-two counties have never recorded as much as 3 inches in one day. This contrast is partly due to the smaller number of observing stations in Ireland. The counties in which a fall exceeding 4 inches has never been recorded are grouped in such a definite geographical manner that there is little doubt that the distribution does represent a distinct climatic factor. In the first group, including most of Ireland, the south-west of Wales and Cornwall, steady rather than intense rainfall is the dominating feature. These counties lying to the west of the land masses are naturally relatively free from intense rains of convectional origin, while the elevation is not sufficiently great to cause very heavy orographic falls. The second group curiously includes the Midlands of England, Gloucester, Hereford, Worcester, Warwick, Rutland and Derby. The explanation seems to be that, while this area is liable to intense rains they are rarely sufficiently sustained to give large amounts in any day. A third zone includes most of the counties along the east of Scotland, as well as the East Riding of Yorkshire.

Daily falls exceeding 5 inches are most frequently found at stations in Cumberland, Westmorland, Carnarvon, Merioneth, Argyll and Inverness, all of them mountainous areas with heavy orographic rains. Falls exceeding 5 inches were recorded on August 26th, 1912, and on June 28th, 1917, at more stations than on any other days. Few people realise that falls of so large an amount are ever experienced in these islands. As a matter of fact, daily falls of as much as 6·5 inches or more, equal to a quarter of London's annual total, have occurred on fifteen different days. The actual largest falls on record are set out below :

LARGEST DAILY FALLS (9 A.M. TO 9 A.M.) ON RECORD

County	Station	Amount	Date
		inches	
Somerset -	Bruton (Sexey's School)	9·56	June 28th, 1917
,, -	Cannington (Brymore House).	9·40	Aug. 18th, 1924
,, -	Bruton (King's School)	8·48	June 28th, 1917
,, -	Aisholt (Timbercombe)	8·39	June 28th, 1917
Inverness -	Loch Quoich (Kinloch-quoich).	8·20	Oct. 11th, 1916
Cumberland	Borrowdale (Seathwaite)	8·03	Nov. 12th, 1897

The first four stations are in relatively dry localities, where the average annual rainfall is 30 to 35 inches, while at the latter stations the average exceeds 100 inches. As in the case of the most intense falls in short periods, the actual largest daily falls have therefore occurred at stations in the drier half of the British Isles. At these four stations as much rain was received in one day as is usually distributed over three months, and such an abnormal state of affairs naturally resulted in considerable damage. Another heavy fall in a normally dry area, 7·31 inches near Norwich on August 26th, 1912, also caused considerable flooding (*Plate I*). At Loch Quoich and Borrowdale the hilly character of the land would lead to a much more rapid run-off than in the former cases.

Some details of the storm of August 18th, 1924, were given in Chapter III. The storm of June 28th, 1917, was much more widespread. It has been computed that during this day 525,000 million gallons, or 2,340 million tons of rain fell over England and Wales. Fortunately the heaviest rain was near the head-waters of several rivers, and the precipitation was thus drained away in diverse directions. Part flowed southwards to Christchurch, and at Gillingham, where the Stour flood was augmented by the spate of several other tributaries, damage of a serious nature occurred. The flood marks at the Town Mills indicate, however, that several earlier floods have been higher. The greater part of the water probably flowed along the Valley of the Brue towards Burnham. At Bruton the valley narrows, and the effect is exaggerated by the design of the town bridge, which confines the river to a narrow channel. The swollen stream broke all bounds and considerable structural damage occurred in the low lying part of the town. In the course of the lower Brue, where the valley broadens, much damage was done to the growing crops for many miles, but flooding, although extensive, was by no means exceptional, for the reason already given. The rainfall was caused by a depression which passed along the English Channel on the 28th, and the heaviest rainfall occurred between 11 p.m. on the 28th and 1 a.m. on the 29th. There is little doubt that soon after this the track of the depression was abruptly modified and subsequently moved to the south-eastward instead of to the north-eastward. On other occasions the heavy rain has occurred to the left of the track, and similar abrupt turns to the right in the track of the associated depression have been observed at about the end of the heavy rain.

The rainfall of October 11th, 1916, in Inverness, was of an entirely different character. The rain fell with a strong and steady S.S.W. wind due to a distribution of pressure dominated by a depression near Iceland and an anticyclone over the Bay of Biscay. In this case the normal prevailing wind was exaggerated with the result that the distribution of rainfall was dictated by the configuration of the land, being thus in direct contrast to the cyclonic rain of June 28th, 1917, which brought the heaviest precipitation on what is normally a dry part of the country. Over much of the Western Highlands more than 3 inches was recorded, while there was less than half an inch over most of the south-eastern half of Scotland, the effect of an intensification of the south-west winds being to increase the normally heavy fall in the mountainous districts at the expense of the lighter fall of the eastern parts. As a result of the storm Fort William was completely isolated, the West Highland Railway, with its branches to Fort Augustus and Mallaig, being rendered impassable for several days by numerous wash-outs. Many of the roads were destroyed by the deep ruts cut by the rain running off quite small catchment areas, and hundreds of tons of débris were carried down to lower levels. The areas of heaviest rainfall were not those in which most damage was reported, since the rain naturally accumulated and caused greater damage in the valleys and also because the full fury of the storm was spent upon the wild mountains and glens beyond any human habitations. Not infrequently the casual visitor to these lonely places finds enormous scars on the hill-side caused by storms which must have attained awful fury. The only indication of their force is afforded by their effect on the ground. It is on record that as the result of a " waterspout " in the Cheviots on July 2nd, 1893, thirty to forty acres of the upper layer of peat were ploughed to a depth of about five feet, and piled in enormous masses. If this damage was really due solely to rain, it must have been exceptionally heavy rain falling practically as a solid mass. It is possible that the rain (or hail) which would normally fall over a large area was held up by rising air currents and deposited over a very small area after the sudden cessation of these currents. Fortunately these storms are very local and the most intense are confined to mountainous regions.

Because the enormous rains of the wet districts have mainly to be transported to the sea, much damage by flooding frequently results in the low-lying districts which have received much less rain. Thus, during the continuous and heavy rain of September 21st, 1927, in the north of England the upper Lune and Balder overflowed their banks but little and presented merely the awe-inspiring spectacle of mountain torrents in flood. Farther down, at Barnard Castle, the River Tees was overflowing and reached the highest point since the memorable flood of the ' eighties. Many of the roads as far east as Darlington were little better than streams and almost impassable to cars. A ten-ton haystack was among the débris carried down to the mouth of the Tees.

In the matter of heavy rains in a day Britain is fairly representative of Europe, but compares very favourably with some parts of the tropics. The largest known daily fall in Europe is 18·3 inches, at Riposto, Sicily, on November 17th, 1910, but falls of 46 inches have been recorded in the Philippine Islands, 32 inches in Hawaii, 36 inches in Queensland, and 30·5 inches in Jamaica, where the fall formed part of a total of 114·5 inches in five days and 135 inches in eight days. All these heavy falls are due to the violent and continued uprush of very moist winds encountering high ground.

The largest totals in the British Isles for periods as long as the month and year are confined to the mountainous districts, especially the English Lake District, Snowdonia and the Western Highlands of Scotland. In each of these districts more than 48 inches of rain has been recorded in one month, or about the usual fall of London for two years.

Similarly, in each of these districts more than 240 inches has been recorded in one year, or as much as falls in London during a decade. Over the whole world the largest recorded total in a month is 336 inches, and in a year more than 900 inches, both at Cherrapunji, in India, in 1861, but the record is open to doubt. A fall of 264 inches, in August, 1841, at this station is, however, properly authenticated. The largest falls in any month on record for London were 8·8 inches at Lee and 8·6 at Deptford in October, 1880, while 8·3 inches was recorded in July, 1918, in Bermondsey. The largest annual total occurred in 1903, when 42 inches was recorded at the Victoria and Albert Museum.

While the distribution of the extreme monthly and annual values is very largely controlled by the configuration of the land, the largest values occurring in the mountainous regions, and the smallest on the plains, nearness to the main tracks of depressions is an important factor in the frequency of days with rain. In the north-west of the British Isles rain falls more frequently than at stations in the south-east. This north-westward increase in the number of rain-days parallel with the increase of rainfall tends to even up the rainfall in an average rain-day, so that in the very wet regions the rainfall is more frequent, being steady and persistent, and the rain is not proportionately more intense than that of the drier regions.

One of the longest runs of rain-days occurred at Eallabus, in Islay, on the west coast of Scotland, where rain fell on every day from August 12th to November 8th, 1923, a period of eighty-nine days. In that year the number of rain-days exceeded 300 in Connemara, and was not far short of a "world record."

The longest runs of little or no rain naturally occur in the regions which are usually dry, but especially in the south-east and east of England, of Wales, of Scotland and of Ireland. The least number of rain-days recorded in any one year was rather less than 100 along the Thames estuary. In 1893, during the spring drought, some twenty stations in the south-east of England, mostly in Kent and Sussex, recorded no rain for a period of fifty days or more. Locally in this district there was a two month's drought from March 17th to May 16th. The year 1893 was unprecedented for the number of periods with little or no rain.

It is fortunate from the point of view of water supply that this region which is most liable to little or no rain coincides roughly with that in which much of the rainfall is retained in the sub-soil. This natural storage compensates in a very marked degree for the more uncertain rainfall, and this is doubtless one of the reasons to which the British Isles owe their comparative freedom from the disastrous effects of droughts. It is interesting to note that even coastal stations are frequently supplied with water pumped from considerable depths. At Sunderland, although the pumping stations are within easy reach of the sea and the water is pumped from below sea level it remains pure.

The comparison of droughts necessitates some criterion other than that of complete absence of rain. The late Mr. G. J. Symons, F.R.S., in dealing with the dry year 1887, suggested that " periods of three or more consecutive months the aggregate of which is less than half the average for that period " should be defined as " Engineer's Droughts." He did not subsequently make use of this definition, but his opinion is worthy of mention in this connection : " There is, I think, little doubt, that droughts will eventually be expressed as fractions or percentages of the mean annual rainfall. . . ." In the case of two stations, London and Glenquoich, the least rainfall in sixty years' records for groups of three or more consecutive months are shown below. The former station is representative of the drier half of the country and the latter station, in the Western Highlands of Scotland, is representative of the wetter regions. The annual average rainfall at the former station is 25 inches, while that at the latter is about 111 inches.

FALLS OF DRIEST CONSECUTIVE MONTHS

Months	Camden Square, London		Glenquoich, Inverness	
	inches	Per cent. of Annual Average	inches	Per cent. of Annual Average
3	1·4	6	5·7	5
4	2·1	9	9·7	9
5	3·5	14	18·9	17
6	4·2	17	22·6	20
7	5·8	24	28·6	26
8	8·2	34	39·9	36
9	9·0	37	50·9	46
10	11·0	45	63·5	57
11	12·1	50	68·7	62
12	14·1	58	74·6	67

Although the actual rainfalls recorded in the driest periods at these two stations are so different, the percentage values are much more nearly alike. In fact, the percentage values for these two stations can be taken as indicating the values likely to occur at stations in any part of the British Isles. At any station therefore the driest period of four months which is likely to occur may be expected to give about 10 per cent., and the driest ten months about half of the average annual rainfall at that station. For a corresponding table for the very dry year 1921, see p. 128.

CHAPTER XIV

CYCLES OF WEATHER

" Oft expectation fails, and most oft there
Where most it promises."
" *All's Well that Ends Well*," Act II, Sc. 1

THE search for cycles of weather is as old as history. Most of these early cycles were astronomical, not only the sun but also the moon and the planets playing their part. In Egypt we may perhaps regard the forecast of seven fat years to be followed by seven lean years as based on a fourteen-year cycle. Coming nearer to our own time, one of our most generally accepted weather periodicities, that of thirty-five years, was known to Sir Francis Bacon and, later still, Luke Howard, who has good claim to be considered as the father of British meteorology, believed in the existence of a cycle of eighteen years. Recently a large number of similar periodicities have been discovered, but in this country at least they do not amount to a great deal, and we are still a long way from basing reliable weather forecasts on periodic phenomena. They are not only small in comparison with the accidental or irregular variations ; they are not even entirely regular and permanent, but have an unfortunate tendency to break down at critical moments and to start again at the wrong time, so that in place of the exact word " periodicity " the more vague term " recurrence " has been coined for them. Nevertheless, they are not without interest, if only for the light which they throw on the natural processes at work in the atmosphere.

Leaving out of account recurrences of a few days or weeks, which are of little importance in determining the character of the whole season or year, we must say a few words about the annual periodicity. In many parts of the world, as in India, the regular alternation of dry and rainy seasons governs the whole life of the community, but in the British Isles the variations from one season to another have little regularity. In England there is a distinct tendency for spring to be drier than the other seasons, but any month may be the wettest or driest of any particular year. During one hundred and thirteen years of observations at Greenwich, from 1815 to 1927 inclusive, the numbers of times each month has been the wettest or driest of the year are as follows :

	Jan.	Feb.	Mar.	April	May	June
Wettest -	1	3	1	2	9	5
Driest -	10	17	10	14	9	14

	July	Aug.	Sept.	Oct.	Nov.	Dec.
Wettest -	19	11	11	26	12	12
Driest -	11	5	7	2	8	5

On one occasion three months were all equally wet, and in another year March and April were equally dry. The prominence of February among the dry months is no doubt due partly to its shortness, but the rarity with which January figures as the wettest month is striking and to many unexpected. Another interesting point about the table is the moderate character of January and March, and the extreme character of July. In spite of the fact that July comes second only to October as the most frequently wet month of the year, while January and March are wettest only once a century, July is the driest month more often than either January or March. The reason is that in July the weather is more often settled than in January, either settled wet or settled dry.

The customary method of measuring periodicities is by their " amplitude." We represent the course of variation by a regular smooth curve, termed a " sine curve," with crests and troughs at equal intervals, and measure the height of the crests above the middle line, or the depth of the troughs below the middle line. Examples of such smooth sine curves as components of the rainfall of England are shown in

Fig. 13. In order that the various periodicities and recurrences discussed in this chapter may be compared with each other, their amplitudes must all be expressed in the same units, and for this purpose the amplitudes are all expressed as percentages of the average rainfall of England during any fixed interval, such as a day, a month or a year. Measured in this way, the amplitude of the annual variation of rainfall in England is 22 per cent., which means that the rainfall per day, or per month, at the crest of the annual variation in October is 22 per cent. greater than the average rainfall per day or per month throughout the year, and is 44 per cent.

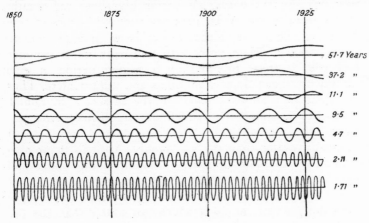

FIG. 13—PERIODICITIES IN THE RAINFALL OF ENGLAND

greater than the average rainfall per day or per month at the trough of the annual variation in April. This figure of 22 per cent. for the annual variation, which we have seen is not at all regular, will serve as a standard of comparison for the amplitudes of the other periodicities in English rainfall. Incidentally, it may be remarked that there is also a six-monthly periodicity with an amplitude of 6 per cent., which contributes towards the relatively small rainfall of September.

The annual recurrence is a true periodicity, which is due to a definite astronomical phenomenon—the varying altitude of the sun at noon in different seasons. In the discussions of

M

the previous chapters it has generally been eliminated by considering the rainfall of any month or season as a percentage ratio of the average rainfall of that month or season during the thirty-five years 1881 to 1915, but it has cropped up now and again, as in the discussion of the relative importance of orographic and thunderstorm rains at different seasons. None of the remaining weather cycles which we have to discuss have the exactitude of true periodicities ; they come within our definition of " recurrences," which are much less regular.

It is possible that there exists one such recurrence of just over twelve months, most probably about $12\frac{3}{4}$ months. It has been found by D. Brunt in monthly values of temperature, where it is chiefly noticeable as giving a tendency for a period of eight years with unusually warm summers and cold winters, followed by a second period of eight years with unusually cool summers and mild winters. There are signs of a similar " cycle of the seasons " in rainfall. When we consider the rainfall of the British Isles as a whole, the six months October to March are as a rule decidedly wetter than the six months April to September. From 1870 to 1926 the average rainfall of the winter half-year was 23·6 inches, that of the summer half-year only 18·7 inches. At intervals of about fifteen years, however, we have one or two summers which are wetter than the preceding winters ; this happened in 1878–79, 1879–80, 1890–91, 1908–09 and 1923–24. A recurrence of $12\frac{3}{4}$ months is so near the periodicity of twelve months that we should have great difficulty in distinguishing it directly, but we see its effects in this alternate accentuation and minimising of the difference between the winter and the summer rains. About 1871 the maximum of the $12\frac{3}{4}$-month period fell in mid-winter, and its minimum in mid-summer. The winter, usually the wettest season, was even wetter than usual ; the summer, normally dry, was drier than usual. Next year the maxima and minima of the $12\frac{3}{4}$-month period came some twenty-two days later, the second year $1\frac{1}{2}$ months later, and after four years the maximum of the $12\frac{3}{4}$-month period came in spring and its minimum in autumn. After another four years, or about 1879, the maximum came in mid-summer and the minimum in mid-winter ; the winter, usually wet, was now relatively dry, and the summer, usually dry, was relatively wet. After a further eight years the position of 1871 was re-established and the cycle recommenced.

It seems probable that the run of wet summers from 1923 to 1927 was largely an expression of the fact that during those years the maximum of the $12\frac{3}{4}$-month period fell in summer. By about 1932 the maximum will fall in winter again, and there will be some prospect of better holiday weather, though, as previously stated, periodicities are rotten reeds from which to fashion pens for writing of future weather.

The next well-known " recurrence " is that of three years, which forced itself on our attention by the remarkable series of wet years, 1888, 1891, 1894, 1897, 1900, 1903, 1906 and 1909, each of which was wetter than the average over the British Isles, while of the remaining years from 1889 to 1908 inclusive, only 1907 even reached an average rainfall, the other thirteen all being drier than usual. This remarkable series seemed to establish a three-year periodicity if anything could, but after 1909 the series broke down. The year 1910 was wetter than 1909, and after that the three-year recurrence was replaced by one of two years. The even years 1910, 1912, 1914, 1916, 1918, 1920 and 1922 were all wetter than the average, while the intervening odd years 1911, 1913, 1917, 1919 and 1921 were all dry, the solitary exception being 1915, which was drier than either 1914 or 1916, but had a rainfall slightly above the average. Before 1888, on the other hand, the wet years seem to have occurred at intervals of about five years : 1872, 1877, 1882 and 1886. The whole thing has a curious air of design, if we could only find the hidden key, but it may equally well be some freak of chance. As we shall see later, however, the two-year periodicity at least seems to be real ; moreover, two, three and five-year periodicities have all been found in the rainfall of other parts of the world. It is also curious that the decreasing intervals between the recurrences of wet years in Britain have run closely parallel with the intervals between successive outbursts of solar prominences. From 1875 to 1892 these outbursts recurred at intervals of 3·7 years, from 1892 to 1900 at intervals of 3·1 years, and from 1905 to 1914 at intervals of 2·5 years.

The close analysis of two hundred years' rainfall over England, which concludes this chapter, shows that the two-year recurrence is really compounded of two periodicities of 1·7 and 2·11 years, respectively, both of which have persisted with very little change through two centuries at least. The combination of these two periodicities gives a series of maxima at intervals of two or three years, at the rate of seven cycles in seventeen years, which resembles rather closely the series of short-period fluctuations actually observed in the annual rainfall of England.

The next important periodicity is one of 4·7 years, which is not very obvious in the annual totals, but is clearly shown by a close analysis. This recurrence is due to the influence of the ice from the East Greenland current, part of which reaches Iceland in abnormally large amounts every fourth or fifth year with almost unfailing regularity. We have already seen in Chapter I that when other conditions are favourable much ice near Iceland tends to give us a long spell of rainy weather. The other factors, such as variations of the Gulf Stream, prevent this 4·7 year periodicity from completely dominating the variations of British rainfall, but it can be found by close inspection.

A rainfall periodicity of considerable importance in this country is that of 9½ years. Its exact cause is doubtful, but it is well developed in many parts of the world, and appears to be related to a movement of the great anticyclones which are found over the oceans in sub-tropical latitudes. It appears probable that these anticyclones swing north and south through a cycle of nineteen years, as maintained by the late Colonel Rawson, but it is difficult to find any adequate reason for such an oscillation. There is a lunar cycle of 18 years 10 days, but that is beside the point. In some subtropical countries this movement is stated to give a nineteen-year periodicity of rainfall, but in England there is very little trace of such a cycle, and it appears that each complete swing of nineteen years gives two maxima and two minima of rainfall. It is easy enough to see that there should be a dry period when the Atlantic anticyclone is farthest north, giving high pressure over this country, but it is not so easy to see why there should be a dry period when the anticyclone is farthest south. It may be that under the latter conditions the fall of pressure from south to north across Britain is smaller than usual, and hence that the amount of orographic rainfall is slight.

The famous eleven-year sunspot cycle is not prominent in the rainfall of England. On the Continent there is a strong tendency for wet years to recur twice during the sunspot cycle, at intervals of five or six years, but even in this modified form the recurrence does not extend to England, for the amplitude of the eleven-year periodicity is 1·6 per cent., and that of the 5½-year periodicity only 1·2 per cent.—a negligible amount. The only part of the British Isles where an eleven-year recurrence is clearly shown is in the West of Scotland. The great Scottish meteorologist Buchan found its influence in the rainfall of Rothesay, in Bute, right through the nineteenth century, the maximum rainfall following about a year after the maximum of sunspots. He found a similar recurrence at other stations in the Western Highlands and the Hebrides, though at most places the measurements of rainfall did not cover a sufficiently long interval to bring it out so clearly as at Rothesay. Since the heavy rainfall at these stations is of the orographic type, caused by moist winds from the Atlantic striking the high ground and being forced to ascend, Buchan naturally expected to find that during and immediately after sunspot maxima south-westerly winds were more frequent than at other times, and an examination of the wind records showed that this supposition was actually correct.

The next recurrence which we have to consider is that of about thirty-five years, which is famous as the Brückner cycle, but which was, in fact, known long before. Francis Bacon wrote : " There is a toy, which I have heard, and I would not have it given over, but waited upon a little. They say it is observed in the Low Countries (I know not in what part), that every five and thirty years the same kind and suit of years and weathers comes about again, as great frosts, great wet, great droughts, warm winters, summers with little heat, and the like, and they call it the prime ; it is a thing I do the rather mention, because, computing backwards, I have found some concurrence."

This circumstantial reference appears to have been over-looked until a few years ago—at least the first mention we have seen of it in recent meteorological work is on the reverse of the title-page of Ellsworth Huntington's book, " Climatic Changes." The recurrence itself was re-discovered and placed on a scientific basis by the late Austrian geographer E. Brückner, whose name it now bears. Brückner found evidence of it in the variations of level of the great European rivers and of the Caspian Sea, and in the fre-quencies of cold winters in Europe, as well as in instrumental observations of rainfall and temperature. He collected a great deal of information from all parts of the world, and came to the conclusion that the variations were almost world-wide in extent, spells of ten to twenty cold, rainy years alternating with similar spells of warm, dry years. The cycle is, however, very irregular in its recurrence ; in Europe, for example, the intervals between successive maxima may vary from fifteen to fifty years. In fact, extensive smoothing away of irregu-larities is necessary before it is possible to see anything approaching a thirty-five-year recurrence.

Brückner's work was so complete that it won general acceptance almost at once. So convinced were British meteorologists of its reality that our average values have ever since been calculated for an interval of thirty-five years, the argument being that such an interval would include one rainy period and one dry period, or one cold period and one warm period, which would neutralise one another and there-fore give us a close approach to the true normal value. If, instead, average values were constructed for an interval of, say, fifty years, they might include two spells of rainy years and only one dry spell, giving too high a normal, or two dry spells and only one group of rainy years, resulting in too low a normal. From the detailed analysis described later, however, it will be seen that in this country at least the argument was not well founded, for the Brückner cycle is relatively unimportant in the rainfall of England. In fact, a periodicity of about fifty years is just twice as effective, and it appears that an interval of fifty years would theoretically give a better normal than one of thirty-five years. As a matter of fact there are quite appreciable differences between the average rainfall of different thirty-five-year periods, not only over the country as a whole, where they may amount to 4 or 5 per cent., but also in the relative distribution of the rainfall over different parts of the country. Practically, however, the choice of a thirty-five-year interval for normals in this country has certain advantages which outweigh theoretical considerations. The great majority of our climatological and rainfall stations depend for their existence on the enthusiasm of amateur meteorologists—without whose disinterested labours the greater part of British climatology, including this book, would not have been possible—and these stations are thus in a sense limited to the maturity of a single life. Hence, while continuous records over a period of thirty-five years are not uncommon, similar records coverin fifty years are rare at private stations, but it is the long homogeneous records which form the backbone of British climatology.

From time to time efforts are made in the Press to exploit the Brückner cycle as an explanation of various untoward happenings in our weather. A moment's consideration will show, however, that the ordinary changes of rainfall from year to year are so great that they must almost entirely mask the gradual long-period fluctuations. Rainfall, like the motorist, is no respecter of cycles, and the driest and wettest of any thirty-five consecutive years are liable to occur at any time. In fact, 1921, the driest year since 1788, came only five years after the latest crest of the Brückner cycle, and five years before the latest crest of the fifty-year recurrence. On the average, the rainfall of any one year over England differs from that of the preceding year by 15 per cent., but the crest of a Brückner cycle receives only 5 per cent. more rain than the trough.

It is remarkable that the Brückner cycle seems to appear far more prominently in what may be called " quasi-meteorological " records than in actual series of instrumental meteorological observations. For example, the *Meteorological Magazine* for March, 1928, contains a diagram illustrating a series of measurements by Mr. E. G. Burtt of the annual growth-rings of a yew tree, two hundred years old, which grew in the Forest of Dean, and for comparison the annual rainfalls in the same district. There is a readily recognisable relation between the curve of tree-growth and the curve of rainfall, the tree growing most rapidly in the dry intervals, but while the rain-gauge seemed to minimise the Brückner cycle, the tree seemed to accentuate it, with well-marked maxima of growth about 1790, 1830, 1860–70 and 1900. A periodicity of thirty-three years, which is identified with the Brückner cycle, is found in the annual rings of growth of the giant *Sequoias*, the " Big Trees," of California, some of which grew for three thousand years. A recurrence of thirty-six years is very clearly shown in the floods of Santiago, in Chile.

The exact length of the Brückner cycle is not known. Brückner himself calculated that it lay between 34·1 and 35·5 years, with a probable average value of 34·8 years, but the California tree rings give only 33·3 years, which has the additional justification of being three times the sunspot cycle. The detailed analysis of two hundred years of rainfall in England, on the other hand, gave it a length of 37·2 years, which is unusually high.

Just as the 1·71 and 2·11 year periodicities are the most important controls of the fluctuations of our rainfall from year to year, so the periodicity of 51·7 years is the most important control of the fluctuations from one generation to

another. We can form a general idea of these fluctuations
back to 1651, and we find that the chief wet spells have
been : 1659 to 1664, 1709 to 1712, 1763 to 1768, 1821 to
1832, 1872 to 1883 and 1922 to 1927. Taking the middle
years of these spells as 1660, 1710, 1765, 1826, 1877 and
1924, we have intervals of fifty, fifty-five, sixty-one, fifty-one
and forty-seven years, which is as near regularity as we are
likely to get in meteorology. By considering the records of
great rains and droughts described in Chapters VI and XII
we can go back a good deal farther, as far as the end of the
fifteenth century, in fact, and still find indications of a
fifty-year recurrence, especially of droughts. Thus, there
were dry spells from 1490 to 1503, 1538 to 1543, 1610 to
1616 and 1651 to 1654, while from Chapter XI we find that
a fourth spell came about 1701 to 1714, and a fifth in 1737
to 1750.

When we come to recurrences of longer period than fifty-
two years, we are faced with the lack of a long series of exact
measurements, and this prevents us from giving a definite
answer to the question whether any boy or girl now living
is likely to see a recurrence of the extraordinarily dry years
from 1737 to 1750. The question is one of vast importance,
for if a single dry year like 1921, falling in the midst of a
series of wet years, suffices to cause grave doubts as to the
adequacy of the water supply of London, only the pen of a
sensational novelist could adequately picture the effect of a
long series of dry years on the, presumably greater, London
of the future.

Such materials as we have, out of which to frame a reply
to the question, fortunately do not give us too great a cause
for anxiety. While nothing can adequately replace instrumental observations, the records of floods and droughts
described in Chapters VI and XII do enable us to form some
idea of the general course of events in the past fifteen hundred
years or so. The general result of such an inquiry seems to
be that while there have been several long periods of dry
years, it is not until we go back to the series of great droughts
from A.D. 651 to 750 that we find a level of rainfall as low

as, or lower than, the first half of the eighteenth century. Exact comparison is of course impossible, but the general impression gained by a critical reader of our annalists and diarists is that these two periods, a thousand years apart, were probably fairly alike in their deficiency of rainfall.

From a study of all the scattered information available, an attempt has been made in Fig. 14 to give a rough idea of the variations of rainfall in this country from Romano-British times down to the present day. The basis of the curve, previous to the first rainfall observations in 1677, is the frequency of great rains and droughts in each century, both relative to each other and to the total number of records of all meteorological phenomena. The actual method em-

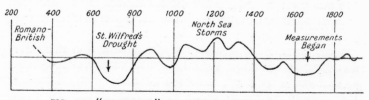

FIG. 14—" RAININESS " IN BRITAIN SINCE ROMAN TIMES

ployed was purely arbitrary, but resulted from a good deal of experiment ; it is briefly described in a note appended to this chapter. In order to distinguish the figures obtained in this arbitrary way from those based on actual rainfall measurements, the former are described as estimates of " raininess." This curve of " raininess " has been modified in a few places by inferences from archæological data, such as Mr. G. M. Meyer's history of water-mills in East Kent, described on p. 155.

It is interesting to note that the wettest period in our history, at least since Romano-British times, would seem to have come almost midway between the two chief dry periods. As we saw in Chapter XI, from 1193 to 1370 the burden of our annalists is " Harvest sore hindered by continued rain." Does this mean that our rainfall waxes and wanes over intervals of a thousand years ? One swallow does not make a summer, and one repetition does not make a periodicity.

If we go back another thousand years from the rainfall maximum about 1200 or 1250, we come to the Roman occupation of Britain, and there has been much controversy about our climate in those days. Much has been made of some rude remarks by Latin authors, but it has also been pointed out with justice that our present climate must seem wet and cold to a visitor from the sunny Mediterranean. Quite recently, however, archæologists have come to the rescue, in response to an appeal published in the *Meteorological Magazine* for January, 1928, and in the issue of *Antiquity* for June of the same year, Dr. J. P. Williams Freeman points to several facts which leave no doubt that in Romano-British times the level of the water in wells dug in the chalk stood much higher than it does at present. Among the interesting examples which he quotes are the finding by General Pitt Rivers of a Roman bucket at the bottom of a well in the Romano-British village of Woodyates, Dorset, 60 feet above the level to which modern wells have to be sunk in the immediate neighbourhood, and the frequency with which some ancient villa or manor, sometimes of Roman origin, is found close to the highest springs of the winterbournes, which run only in the wettest seasons. Since we cannot suppose that such sites were chosen for the sake of springs which broke out once in several years, they must then have been perennial or nearly so. Thus we have some evidence of two wet periods separated by a thousand years, alternating with two dry periods separated by a thousand years, but further than that we cannot go. There may have been a dry period in Britain about 300 B.C., but if so, it has left no trace.

The series of two hundred annual values of rainfall over England, published in the *Meteorological Magazine* for February, 1928, under the somewhat dismal title " Two Centuries of Rain," form an admirable basis for the study of the periodicities from two to fifty years described above. The process of examination, known as Fourier analysis, is somewhat lengthy and laborious, and only a table of the final results can be given here. Apart from those of 12 and of $12\frac{3}{4}$ months, the seven most important periodicities found, with their amplitudes and the last year of maximum, are as follows :

Periodicity	Amplitude	Last Maximum
Years.	Per cent.	
51·7	4·7	1926
37·2	2·4	1916
11·1	1·6	1927
9·51	3·4	1925–26
4·7	3·5	1923–24
2·11	3·9	1926
1.705	6·0	1927 (Spring)

The amplitudes given for the last two periodicities are not their true amplitudes, but those which they introduce into the annual variation, a much smaller quantity. A periodicity of 5·1 years was found to persist with great regularity from about 1825, its amplitude being 2·0 per cent., but before 1825 it could not be traced, and it has therefore been omitted from the table.

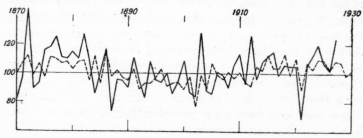

FIG. 15—RAINFALL OF ENGLAND, 1870–1927
OBSERVED AND COMPUTED

From the data given above, it is easy to calculate what the rainfall of each year would have been had it been entirely governed by these seven periodicities. The contributions made by each of the seven to our rainfall from 1870 to 1927 are shown by the wave-like curves of Fig. 13. In Fig. 15 these curves are combined to give a reconstruction of the rainfall (broken line), while that actually experienced is shown for comparison by the full line. It will be seen that while there is a certain amount of agreement, especially in the general trend of the two curves, the details are often woefully at fault. The wet period of the 'seventies and early 'eighties is faithfully reproduced by the calculated curve, and the dry period of the 'nineties is shown fairly well, thought with some differences of detail. The very dry year 1887 is represented on the calculated curve by a drop to only just below normal, while even worse, the very wet year 1903 is also calculated as slightly drier than normal. On the other hand, the dry year 1921 is well represented by a pronounced dip in the calculated curve, and the wet spell from 1922 to 1927 is also fairly well reproduced.

The calculated curve has been continued to the year 1930, but with the cautionary examples of 1887 and 1903 in mind, it will be understood that this is in no sense a forecast. Hence the fact that the curve dips quite decidedly after 1928 is merely to be regarded as a tendency, which may or may not come to fruition. The curve is based on the analysis of two hundred years of data, and gives grounds for optimism, but in meteorology periodicities are synonymous with pitfalls, and the optimism must be tinged with doubt.

NOTE ON THE METHOD OF CALCULATION OF "RAININESS"

FROM A.D. 9 to 1650 there are 1·8 times as many records of droughts (d) as of great rains and wet years (w), hence the numbers of the latter in each century were multiplied by this figure to restore the balance. As a standard with which to compare the difference ($1·8w - d$) we took, not the number of records of wet years and droughts alone, but the total number (n) of all meteorological records in that century, since it appeared that if there were, say, ten records in a century, all of which referred to droughts, this century was presumably drier than if only two referred to droughts and the remaining eight to elements other than rainfall. Finally, it was found that when records were few, the disproportion between w and d tended to be greater than when records were many, the disproportion being roughly, inversely proportional to the square of the number of records. Hence the difference ($1·8w - d$) was divided by $\sqrt{n}$.

For the very dry eighth century this method gives a figure of $- 3·1$. Since it does not seem probable that this century was any less dry than the fifty years 1701 to 1750, for which we have calculated the rainfall as 93 per cent. of the standard normal, it appears that these estimates should be doubled in order to make them, very roughly, comparable with rainfall statistics in size, though not of course in reliability. Hence for the "raininess" we obtain the expression

$$R = 100 + \frac{2 (1·8w - d)}{\sqrt{n}}$$

THE END

INDEX

N